To Lois Keidan

WITHDRAWN

There's often more than a whiff of impending apocalypse to the preposterous spectacle proposed in Tim Etchells' Vacuum Days.

Responding to the political, social and media landscape of 2011 proved a perfect sounding board for the artist's caustic comical take on troubling and strange real-life material. Through the year capitalism's fear factory was working overtime to keep its citizens in a pliable state of anxiety and distraction while the disasters (natural and man-made), upheavals (expected and unexpected), revolutions (triumphant and failed) and crises (economic and otherwise) just kept on coming.

From January to December, as one news frenzy or media circus ended, the next one was already in progress. Shifting from absurdist critique to dark comedy, Vacuum Days relentlessly maps the territory of contemporary disaster and dysfunction – from the ongoing Eurozone crisis to the Fukushima disaster, from Bird Flu scares to the British Royal Wedding, from the killing of Osama Bin Laden to the bizarre death of Michael Jackson, from the Arab Spring to the summer of riots in the UK.

Tim Etchells (1962) is an artist and a writer based in the UK. His work shifts between performance, visual art and fiction. He has worked in a wide variety of contexts, notably as the leader of the world-renowned performance group Forced Entertainment.

For more information see:
www.timetchells.com
www.forcedentertainment.com

ENGLAND BECOMES THE DAWN

'Muzacal farewell to yesteryear'
a chorus of Rottweilers sing a medley of tunes by Slade,
Trumpton, N-Dubz, Fartarse, MC Helicopter & Vera Lyn [Sic]

PLUS

Girls Wearing Nothing But Ugg Boots
Bathe Each Other Slowly in a Bucket of Melted Snow

—

IN THE BASEMENT

'Live' from Belarus
President Alexander Lukashenko
Explains His Commitment to Democracy
in Language That Anyone Can Understand

No Latecomers. No Questions from the Floor.
With an introduction by Vladimir Putin

—

Festive INTERNET Special
Puke on the Pavement
'a new years flickr vomit stream'

Big Cheap & Absolutely Fuck-Off

FIREWORKS

More Impressive For Their Noise Than For Their Beauty
Not Suitable for People With Nerves, Depression, Shell Shock,
Post-Traumatic Stress Disorder, Dogs, Cats or Children

—

Drive-In Movie Screening at the Ground Zero Mosque

BRING ME THE HEAD
OF JULIAN ASSANGE

18 Certificate. Contains nudity and scenes of the internet.

—

In the Annex
CUT TO THE BONE
Doctors with Knives Exact 50% CUTS
out of anything that moves

PLUS

'In Bed with Hugh Hefner'
Nightmare of a Blonde Girl

Roman Theme Orgy
bring your own hemlock
valet chariot parking

ALL NIGHT FIGHT NIGHT

People With No Dignity
vs
People With No Hope

Men With No Trousers
vs
Women With No Chance

—

Hangover Cures of the Rich & Supposedly Famous

Inc. Puff Daddy, Natalie Imbruglia, Wes Craven & Barbara Windsor
Free Download - just enter bank numbers, sort code, date of birth,
home address & social security number

—

IN THE FOYER
Bankers Bailout Masterclass: All New Voodoo Economics

—

Buy None Get One Free
Take Two Now Get More Tomorrow
Rest Tomorrow Work Yesterday
Pay Tomorrow Rest Forever

Run 'Wild' Run Free
Genetically Modified Salmon Race

—

Birds Poisoned With Red Bull
Bulls Poisoned with Bird Shit

—

Cage Fighting Celebrities
with nearly identical names

Madonna **vs** Maradona
Jack White **vs** Barry White

—

all the way from parliament
IN THE CAR PARK/OUTDOOR SPECTACULAR

Mr. Nick Clegg (Liberal Democrat)
vs
Mr. David Cameron (Conservative)

Winner Stays On
'Barefist'
Wanking Contest

Judged by Margaret Thatcher from Her Death Bed
The Judges decision is FINAL
NO CORRESPONDENCE WILL BE ENTERED INTO

A THIEF PARADED IN THE STREETS SO THAT ALL MAY LAUGH AT HIS UNFASHIONABLE TRACKSUIT & CHEAP FALLING-TO-BITS TRAINERS

—

CUT PRICE COMEDY CLUB
Fart Jokes, Wife Jokes, Shit Jokes, Spastic Jokes,
Foreigner Jokes, Farting Wife Jokes, Shitting Spastic Jokes,
Farting Shitting Spastic Foreigner Jokes etc.

—

ALL DAY & ALL NIGHT
Arsonists Posing as Firemen
'Musical Revue'
With music by Justin Bieber & some lyrics by Sir Andrew Lloyd Webber
Based on an original book by Adam Smith. No Latecomers.

FOCUS ON THE POSITIVE

Inc. Speeches about Love & How People Should Be Nice To Each Other
'Relaxing Atmosphere', Dried Flowers, Warm Colours & Partly Subdued Lighting

Solo Piano Music
by
Bert Hampernickel & Beryl Grimsby

—

The Girls & Boys
of the Dewsbury Academy of Song, Deportment & Dance

present

A BALLET DEPICTING RECENT YULETIDE TRAVEL CHAOS

—

Partial Demolition of a Largely Pre-Fabricated Building

Complex Re-Re-Rental of An Already Stolen Yet Borrowed & Part-Re-Rented Bicycle

—

FREE ENTRANCE for the FIRST 600 UNACCOMPANIED Women
Terms & Conditions May Apply

ALL NIGHT TAG-TEAM WRESTLING
Made Visible By Means of ARTIFICIAL LIGHT

WOMEN IN BURKAS

VS

YOUTHS WEARING LONG SNORKEL PARKAS

Winners Stay ON. Losers Buy The Drinks. Free iPod for all Contestants.

—

PREVIEW SCREENING
TUG-OF-LOVE HOSPITAL DOCU-DRAMA OF THE MONTH

BROKENHEART
AT WOUNDED KNEE

sponsored by Pfizer, GlaxoSmithKline & Kleenex

—

IN THE FOYER
German Idiot Dance Troupe
interpret
Songs from 'Bruce Springsteen The Musical'
Not Exactly Suitable for Children

—

IN THE BASEMENT
BRAINWASHING FOR BEGINNERS
Bring Your Own Test Subjects. Chemicals Provided.

GALA NIGHT

The Peter Grasping Award for Pre-Teen Entrepreneurs (Sic)

&

The Rebecca Slovenly Leadership Award

Prizes presented by H.R.H. Diana Princess of Wales (deceased),
Courtney Love & Courtney Cox.
Contest Open to Everyone. No Foreigners.

—

In the Café

Rubber Chicken in a Basket
served with
a Dressing of Reconstituted Protein-Free Milk Substitute,
Finely Grated Low Calorie Cling Film
& a Reduction of Unfiltered Tap Water *

*Not suitable for Vegetarians

—

In the Bar

REGGAE DISCO / 'RASTAFARIAN' RED STRIPE PROMOTION

Outside

Neighbourhood Watch Watch ©
Free Range Criminals Out-Snoop the Snoopers

BALLET SHOW

Ballet of Antelopes
Ballet of Robots
Ballet of Centipedes
Ballet of Fools
Ballet of Riot Police*

*plus other ballets t.b.c.

—

PLUS

Paedophile Priests Advice Session
How To Get Away With It
&
Important Video Message
'Rambling & Largely Inaudible Apologies from a Pope'

—

On the Big Stage

Two Beautiful Youths
in a Choreographed Simulation of
Economic Freefall

NO SAFETY NETS OR HARNESSES. NO CRASH HELMETS.
feat. Music by Lady Gaga's Brother, Skank Pubis & MC Dandelion

On the Main Stage

THE ART OF DISAPPEARANCE

Vanishing Acts & other Sleights of Hand & International Law
perpetrated by MOSSAD, FSB, MOIS, MI5 etc.

With 6 'Glamorous Assistants', 60 Doves & 66,000 Hawks

Sponsored by 2 Local Airlines & an Otherwise Reputable Truck Rental Firm

—

On the Small Stage

Human Origami

Two Dozen Prisoners
Kept Six Months in a Cell Designed for Three

PAGE THREE MODELS
in STRESS POSITIONS

Playdates of the Month
Bound, gagged, handcuffed & SUBJECTED to EXTRAORDINARY rendition

—

In the Foyer

Klaus Wunderbar on his Electrified Piano

Adult Education
Get Down on the Sand Motherfucker:

Roadblock Arabic for Beginners

Lesson One: Questioning, Insinuating, Accusing & Intimidating

—

All Day On the Big Screen
Fly on a Wall productions present

OPEN HEART SURGERY OF A MINOR CELEBRITY

Inc.: doctor p.o.v. cam., aorta cam., knife cam., nurse cam., ass cam.

—

In the Foyer
Pigeons Trapped in a Football Of Razor Wire

Boom Time is All the Time

A SELECTION OF TALENTED INVESTMENT BANKERS GROSSLY INFLATED USING A HOME-MADE SIPHON & AN ELECTRIFIED WATER PUMP UNTIL THE CIRCUMFERENCE OF THEIR WAISTLINES IS EXACTLY EQUAL TO THE SIZE OF THEIR BONUSES*

*Or until they burst, whichever is sooner

"The Period of Apology & Remorse is OVER"

6 BUCKETS OF COCAINE & A TROUGH OF CHAMPAGNE for ALL contestants
Public School Boys Get Double. Just SHUT UP You KNOW it makes SENSE.

—

ECONOMIC HARDSHIP: THE OPERA

Duration: 3 years with no interval
Note: Once admitted to the auditorium patrons are kindly forbidden to leave.

Floods, Tsunami & Other Natural Disasters
Depicted in a Dance
Performed by Underprivileged Children
Approx 63.3% of Proceeds to Charity

Original music by Bono's Gardener & a Man That Knew Bob Geldof's Plumber

—

Important Workshop: Sleeping With The Enemy
SAFE & ABOVE ALL ETHICAL
"METHOD ACTING
FOR UNDERCOVER COPS"
No Kissing on the MOUTH, No Penetration, No Fibbing.
Also Inc. How to Sound Green & Crusty, How to Talk all Street etc.

Organised by R.A.D.A, 'Lee Strasberger (sic) Studio' etc.
in Collaboration with The National Public Order Intelligence Unit & The Metropolitan Police Force
Guest Speakers: Sir Michael Caine, Sir Bob Hoskins or Sir Ray Winestone (sic) depending on price

—

Ebony & Ivory Revisited
Michael Jackson (deceased) duets with Mick Hucknall t.b.c.

Mount Everest
Secretly Ground Down into Dust
STOLEN
&
Reconstituted Elsewhere

—

ON THE BIG SCREEN
Explaining DEATH To VERY Young Children
FEAT. TWO Doctors, a Priest, a Drunk, a Drunk Priest & a Stand up Comedian

—

DIY SPECIAL
ATTIC, BASEMENT & OUTHOUSE CONVERSION
'Make The Most of Your Property'

Simple, Safe & ECONOMICAL Ways to Construct Your Own Prison Cells,
Isolation Ward, Quarantine or Punishment Block.

(NEXT WEEK: **'The Suburban Gulag'**)

—

Oil Spill in the Shape of a Mickey Mouse
Oil Spill in the Shape of a Christmas Tree*

*plus other oil spills t.b.c.

MASSIVE TOTAL & ABSOLUTE AMBIVALENCE

—

SONGS ABOUT DEAD MEN
BY WOMEN THAT WERE NEVER ALIVE

—

Best of the Internet Part Six
Pets on Drugs
Inc. Stoned Chihuahua, Tripping Goldfish, Parrot-on-the-Nod,
Alligators on Angel Dust etc.

—

A Sprinkle of Ostentatious Wristwatches
Served over a Bed of Credit Cards

'Live' in Concert

Glenn Basilica & His Big Band

Plus Support

'The Greatest THING Since Sliced Bread or Processed Cheese'

New, Olde & Old Old Labour United

feat. Keir Hardie on Drums, Gordon Brown on Drums, Ed & David Miliband on Drums,
Michael Foot on Drums, Tony Benn on Drums & Tony Blair on Drums
with vocals by Shirley Willams & Diane Abbott

—

From the Mountains of Afghanistan
ALL NEW Best of
Drone-Cam. Surveillance Footage
The Hottest Fire-Fights, Most Brutal Murders & Most Confused-Looking Donkeys

—

In the Canteen
Cordon Bleu Prison Chefs Cookery Contest
Big Ronnie vs Little Eddie
Special Prize: Two Years Remission
A Maximum Security Event, sponsored by Maxim, Birds Eye, Sabatier & Moulinex

ABUSING THE WELFARE SYSTEM

Nine Experienced & Shameless Scroungers Share Top Tips for a Life of 'Dole Luxury' Inc. teenage pregnancy, maximising your methadone, how to fail at a job interview, etc.

Sponsored by Daily Mail. Free Entrance for all Roma, White Trash & Migrant Jobseekers.

&

Specialist Workshop for Prospective Claimants of Disability Benefit

The Effective Non-Permanent Simulation of Blindness

Dr. Morton Weismuller MD

plus

An Experiment involving Nerve Gas and Prisoners

City Traders Read Karl Marx and John Maynard Keynes

A Dance by Homeless Blokes wrapped in Tartan Blankets

A Series of Explosions Whose Cause Remains Unknown

—

TARZAN THE APE MAN
'ON ICE'
No Latecomers. No refunds.

FRUITLESS INFINITIES

'Late Capitalist Discotheque'

8 'til LATE. 200 Bars, 83 Dance floors, 50 VIP Rooms

&

World's LARGEST underclass HOLDING TANK

No admittance without an Identity Card

—

In the Car Park

MOTORISED DONKEY RACE

Fastest Donkey Wins a Prize

No Robots. No Horses

First LIVING Donkey to Cross the Line is DECLARED THE VICTOR

Sponsored by L'Oreal & Givenchy

PRIZES AWARDED by Sir Anthony Hopkins & Dale Winton

—

Free Concert
Of Freely Improvised
Free Jazz Music

Admission £22.50. No Concessions. Disabled Parking.

On the Big Screen

Arab World
High Stakes Only
Winner Takes All
Democracy Domino Tournament

1st Contestant: Tunisia. 2nd Contestant: t.b.c.
**Random Members of Old Regime, Spurious Advisors
& International Vested Interests etc. ALL Welcome.
STRICTLY First Come First Served**

—

'Movie Bucket' Double Bill
Straight to Illegal Download

Idle Daydreams of a Bone Idle Baggage Handler
Starring Dick Carbonara, Antonio D'Aglio Olio, Nancy Pesto & Sara Rigatoni Farfalle

PLUS

Revisionist History of a Psychotronic Babylon
The Second-Assistant-Director's Cut. Now in 3-D. Digitally Re-Mastered in Quadraphonic Sound.

—

DOGS that SHOULD BE IN Quarantine FIGHT PAUPERS
FOR SCRAPS that should have been INCINERATED

IN THE BASEMENT

AN OBJECT THAT IS MAINLY HOLES

Free admission – philosophers and over 18s only. Not suitable for children or idiots.

—

Community Dance Project / Young Offenders Job Creation Scheme
With a Choreographic Floor Pattern Based on the Cracks in 10,000 Paving Slabs
Music by Walrus, Beethoven, Laser & Seminal Others t.b.c.

"STREET TALK" DISCUSSION EVENT
feat. SIX well QUALIFIED
ECONOMISTS
with their FACES PRESSED
HARD
into the REALITY of the SIDEWALK

Hosted by Two Blokes That Once Mugged Jeremy Paxman
Theme Tune Composed by Michael Nyman

—

OUTRAGEOUS DISCOUNTS ON PRE-SELECTED POINTLESS ITEMS
"EVERYTHING" MUST "GO"
STOCK LIQUIDATION / ASSET VAPOURISATION

Olde Fashioned Customised VIP Electronic Tagging Bracelets by Versace, Compton & Watermelon
Biodegradable Underwear by Slut, Viberton & Raspberry
Solar-Powered Landmines by Cross, George & Siddenham
Spermicidal Face Cream by Audrina Patridge & Kurt Mongoose

Ladies & Gentlemen etc. of 'The Pitsmoor School for Belly Dancing'

PRESENT

A Season in HELL

Adapted for the stage by Mr. Frederick Constance
Translated by a friend of his brother

PLUS

Laughter of an Undertaker

&

ALL NIGHT STAGFLATION

—

IN THE ANNEX

'DOUBLE TROUBLE' CAREER–SUICIDE TAG–TEAM WRESTLING

SELF-MEDICATING NURSES
vs
SELF-IMMOLATING FIREMEN

Scenes Of Debauchery

As Glimpsed Through a Tear In The Fabric of Social & Economic Reality

—

Weight Watchers All NUDE Ariel Burlesque
Not Suitable for Children

Unpalatable Facts About St. Petersburg

Unpalatable Physics Experiments

Unpalatable Risotto Made With A Substance
That No-One Can Really Identify

—

In the Annex:

Adult Re-Education
Inc. Pole Dancing for Housewives, Stand up Comedy for Drunks etc.

PLUS

MILITARY-STYLE ADVANCED AQUA-AEROBICS

THE INEVITABLE RISE OF THE YOUTH UNEMPLOYMENT FIGURES
As Dramatised by Ex-Students of a Now Defunct Mime School

—

CELEBRITY SOUP KITCHEN
EST. 1848.
PATRONS: JAMIE OLIVER & OLIVER TWIST (DECEASED)

"Free Soup for Homeless or Persons Living in Squalor"

Canned MEAT, Jaundice & Liquorice Flavour Only
NB. Strictly One Bowl Per Beggar

—

Teach Your Pets to Speak FRENCH
COURSE DEVISED BY A GENUINE FRANCOPHONE
120 CDs & a BOOKLET – ALSO AVAILABLE IN BRAILLE
COURSE NOT SUITABLE FOR WOLVES

—

ARSON FOR BOYS
Night School Reopens After the Fire

Christianity Youth Group Discussion Night

Is Masturbation Against the Bible?
Is it Against the Bible to Masturbate?
Is it Illegal to Masturbate against the Bible?
Is it Legally Biblical to Be Against Masturbation?

etc.

PLUS

EX-SATANISTS REPENT
&
SEX-ARSONISTS REPEAT

—

Old Dogs Perform New Tricks

—

Live Concert
Stormy Weather Sisters
feat. All New Best-Of Severe Weather Warnings Vol. 7
Set to Music by Hassan I-Sabbah & Sung by a CHOIR

Anti Terrorist Burlesque

BLINDFOLD MEMBERS

of the

SECURITY SERVICES STRIP SEARCH

NON-SCHENGEN STRIPPERS

in

STRICT SLOW MOTION

feat. the Footloose & Fancy Free Big Band Sound
of Kev Woollerton & His High-Fidelity Orchestra

Free Admission to Chelsea Pensioners. No Arabs. Patriots Only.

—

Famous DJs Advise

Songs to Play in the Inevitable Rain. Songs to Play on a Lover's Departure.
Songs abt the Palestinian Authority & Its Negotiations With Israel

& etc. t.b.c.

—

ON THE SMALL STAGE
a gulf of silence opened up between two brothers

Herge's Adventures of Myxomatosis

STOMACH TURNING 3-D IMAX All-Action Animation
from PIXAR / GAGARIN STUDIOS
"The entertainment finance consortium that part-financed Avian Flu and Avian Flu 'Flew' II"
Digital Projection. Nonsensurround Sound.
Free Entrance & Surprise 'Myxomatosis Gift–Bag' for Under Fives

—

IN THE BASEMENT
All the Way from the HOLY LAND

Prime Minister Benjamin Netanyahu
Explains With Great Patience
For Those That Did Not Get It The First Time
WHY ISRAEL is EXEMPT FROM THE BURDENS OF COMMON SENSE & INTERNATIONAL LAW

9-Hour Lecture. Standing Room Only. No Interval. No Questions. No Cameras.
No Admission without the Proper Paperwork

—

OUTSIDE (LOCATION T.B.C.)

POLICE beat a JOURNALIST
smashing her glasses and seizing her Camera

Alarm Testing PARTY

Inc. Fire, Burglar & Intruder Alarms

Everyone Welcome. Smash up cars, shops and private residences. Absolute Free-For-All.

Participants Responsible for their own Legal Fees. Sponsored by ADT.

—

DAVOS-THEME DISCO

Inc. World Music Chill Out Room

PLUS

International LATE NIGHT CABARET

Egypt on the High Wire

(plus other countries t.b.c)

—

Seven Deadly Sins of the Internet

Semi-Comic Opera. With Music by Tim Berners-Lee, Henry Purcell & Henry Mancini

Sung by TWO white guys from BOLTON with what looks like CEREBRAL PALSY

All proceeds to the Manager's Retirement Fund

—

GAY RIGHTS UGANDA – Seminar Cancelled

On The Main Stage

MUBARAK TALKS SHIT FOR AS LONG AS ANYONE WILL LET HIM

PLUS

Talented Pets
Horse That Can Play Asteroids
Rabbit That Can Use A Mobile Phone
Dogs That Can Order Pizza
Gerbils That Can Load & Fire An Automatic Weapon

Generalised Transfiguration

—

SPECIAL MOVIE PRESENTATION

Genuine Pre-Autopsy X-Rated Bio-Medical & Erotical Sensation
"Inside Margaret Thatcher"

A BIZARRE EXPERIMENT IN MEDICAL SOCIALISM

Re-Distribution of Health

Sick People Made a Bit Better & Otherwise Well People Made To Feel Poorly

Sponsored by Fox News

Introduced by Sir Arthur Conan Doyle (Deceased)

—

In The Annex
Nine-Hour Meeting of a Harsh & Pointless Sub-Committee

No Refreshments. No Ventilation. Non-Simultaneous Translation.

—

CELEBRITY ORGAN DONORS

The Kidney of Mel Gibson (Buy One Get One Free)
The Eyes of Laura San Giacomo
Heart of Phillip Glass
Liver of Lindsay Lohan

& Other Donors t.b.c.

Paris Hilton & Ivanka Trump Visit Cairo To See If They Can Help

(Whirlwind Tour: Next Stops Tunis, Baghdad, Afghanistan, Rotherham & the Mexican / US Border)

—

Debilitating Confusion / Howling of Banshees

—

GENERALISED ABJECTION

—

Britney Spears in Concert (Re-Enactment)

Re-Run White Water Car & Home Rafting from Australia

—

OPENING OF A NIGHTCLUB CALLED

Privilege

VIP LIST ONLY. No Smack Addicts or Glue Sniffers.
Baseball Caps MUST Be Worn With The Pointy Bits Facing FORWARDS
Jeans MUST Be Worn With a BELT and Not Showing Half Your UNDERPANTS

The Shit of the RICH Shovelled Into The Open Mouths of Gullible Idiots

Bring Your Own Excrement. Spades Provided.

—

Bikini Blindfold
Flat Pack Furniture Assembly Contest

Who Can Get It Up Fastest?

JUDGED by Jordan a.k.a. 'Katie Price' & The Brother of a Bloke from Big Brother

—

In the Car Park

Young Offenders Do Push Ups In The Pouring Rain

Single Mothers Do Sit Ups in a Jelly–Filled Paddling Pool

'HOMELESS STYLE' POTATO ALCOHOL
Served in Rotten Re-used Supposedly Disposable Cups

GREAT NEW SOUTHBANK ATTRACTIONS

The London Throat
The London Ear
The London Mouth

Plus other LONDON ORGANS & ORIFICES t.b.c.
Guaranteed Thrills, Frills & Edutainment for ALL the Family. No Children.

—

Free Concert in the Car Park (Pay & Display)
feat. ONCE In A Lifetime POIGNANT DUET

President Hosni Mubarak WITH special guests Peter, Paul & Mary (Deceased)
Leaving On A Jet Plane
Lyric & Tune by John Denver. Bags Packed by Egypt.

PLUS

The National Anthem of England
Played on a Xylophone of Bones

Conducted by D. Cameron. Musical arrangement by Thatcher & Rachmaninov.

The Lord is Greater Than Money
& Other Readings from the Emoticon Bible

God's Word Translated For Internet
Now with ASCII Characters Only

Next week – Bhagavad-Gita, Qur'an etc.
All Welcome. No Sinners.

—

Gladiatorial Combat
of The Recent Unemployed

Free Hot Dogs & A Warm Drink For All Contestants

—

In the basement

Emotional Weight-loss Clinic / Economic Asphyxiation

—

Haitian Earthquake Demons in Concert

Delirium Tremens Orchestra Play New Songs By Silvio Berlusconi & Dmitry Medvedev

No Disabled Access. Win An iPod Shuffle or £20 Record Token.

—

CURSE OF BLOCKED DRAINS
&
BLOCKED ARTERIES

—

Forgetting as a POLITICAL TOOL

Burning Fires of MYOPIA

—

In the Basement
Children Playing with Hand-Grenades

Cut Price 'Cordon Bleu' Cookery Evening

Oven Ready Medical Off-Cuts
"Grilled, Fried & Boiled in a Bag"

Served in a Sauce of Vintage Unfiltered Chernobyl Rain Water

PLUS

Selections from
The Carcinogens Cookbook

—

In the BASEMENT

Obese Persons Dance Marathon

Money Printing at Home (Workshop)

Debt Management (Workshop)

Anger Management (Workshop)

'Quantitative Easing'

Dubbed Laughter / Increased Liquidity

Big Stage Lecture Series

WAYS TO MAKE MONEY

**Inc. WAYS TO MAKE MONEY ON THE INTERNET
WAYS TO MAKE MONEY ON A STREET CORNER
WAYS TO MAKE MONEY FROM FAMILY & FRIENDS
WAYS TO MAKE MONEY USING BLACK MAGIC
WAYS TO MAKE MONEY FROM YOUR KIDS
WAYS TO MAKE MONEY FROM YOUR PETS
WAYS TO MAKE MONEY USING A STICK
WAYS TO MAKE MONEY USING A PLASTIC KNIFE
& WAYS TO MAKE MONEY USING A CHEMISTRY KIT**

—

SEMI-POLITICAL THEATRE

'Bargain Hunters
of the Underclass'

Starring Vanessa Redgrave, Jane Fonda & Elizabeth Hurley
Free entrance & a Cup-a-Soup for the long-term unemployed

ABYSMAL VELOCITY

Not suitable for Pensioners

—

TV–Dinnertime SPECIAL

"Re-Hashed Non-Recyclable Press & Marketing Materials From a Once Powerful but Now-Defunct Quango"

Shredded, Boiled, Mashed & Sprinkled with Inkjet Toner
(Served with a NON-OPTIONAL side-dish of Horse Liver in Nicotine & Regurgitated Residues)
Free Can of COKE, PEPSI or LOCAL EQUIVALENT

—

Celebrity Botox Distortion
Who will go the furthest?
Human Hall of Mirrors. No Surgery Required.
Cash Prizes. Sponsored by Homebase.

PLUS

Miss Teen Taipei & Miss Teen U.S.A. Trade Places in Trans-National Costume

DRUNKS vs TODDLERS
RAPID MOTION CENTRIFUGE CHALLENGE
Last One to Vomit Wins a Prize

PLUS

6 Short Dancers on Stilts /
3 Badly Wounded Mime Artists Rolled
In Quicklime & Salt

—

Emotional Striptease of a Former Dinner Lady

PLUS

Vulnerable Adults on DANGEROUS ICE

—

Men of Dubious Intelligence
Burn Bridges They Haven't Even Crossed

TAX CUTS FOR THE WEALTHY & PRISON FOR THE REST

Cameron, Clegg & Co. Explain Their Policies AGAIN
& HOW they have been WIDELY Misinterpreted by Ignorant People etc. etc.

PLUS

BONFIRE OF THE SOCIALITES /
QUAGMIRE OF THE SOCIALISTS

"WANKERS IN BED WITH BANKERS"

**HARDCORE MONEY-MARKET 'BONUS PORN'
CALL-GIRLS & OLD BOYS VIAGRA FLOTATION
ALL-ANAL DOUBLE-DIP TORY-ON-LIB-DEM ACTION
STRICT 'FINANCIAL SERVICES'
& FREE HAND RELIEF FOR EVERYONE ON £90K PLUS**

—

RULE BRITANNIA / EVISCERATE THE POOR
(Didactic Cabaret from Eton)

Cowboy Wheelclampers of the Prairie

**Directed by John Forde (sic)
& STARRING a series of UNSUSPECTING motorists**

Headless Corpses in a Taxi Cab

Sleep Cycles of the Rich & Famous

Family ticket for all GENUINE families. Free Popcorn & Painkillers for ALL.

—

A NEW CONCERT OF OLD MUSIC

BY

HARRISON BERTWHISTLE, JOHN ENWISTLE (Deceased) & JOHN BARRY (Deceased)

SUNG WITH AN UNNECESSARY LIBRETTO BY SNR. FABRIZIO FLABBERGASTE
DEPICTING IN HORRIFYING DETAIL THE DWINDLING NUMBERS OF PEOPLE USING MYSPACE

TRANSLATED FROM ITALIAN USING GOOGLE TRANSLATE

All Seats Restricted View

Sweat Shop Soap Opera

Heartwarming Light Comedy
from the Lives of Modern-Day Slaves

PLUS

NEW DRAMA FROM TALENTED EURO–MIME TROUPE

The Invisible Hand of the Market Pushes Children Over a Cliff

Music by Crisis, Moron & Horlicks. No Latecomers.

ALL NUDE LIVE SHOW
BEAUTY SECRETS
OF THE SUPER MODELS
Gisele Bündchen, Karolína Kurková,
Miranda Kerr, Marisa Miller
& Doutzen Kroes
BATHE NAKED
IN THE FRESH TEARS
OF ORPHAN CHILDREN

NOT Suitable for Orphans. Sponsored by Aloe Vera.

—

DANCING WITH THE ARMY
'Democratic Musical from Egypt'

Written by The People
Early Scenes Ghost Written by Hosni Mubarak, Omar Suleiman & some C.I.A. Handlers
Stage Managed with help from Field Marshal Mohamed Hussein Tantawi, HAMAS & The Muslim Brotherhood

& INTRODUCING Wael Ghonim

FREE CONCERT

"Debt Music Concerto"
by Mssrs. Rachmaninov & Insolvency

Played by a Leper on a Gypsy Violin
Intermission Special feat. Strippers, Folk Dancers, Laser Show & FREE hot dogs

PLUS

The Return of Cretinous Logic

—

IN THE BASEMENT

**Two Blokes Who Look Like They Might Be Immigrants
Subjected to Vigilante 'Homestyle Retina Scans'
By Means of a Retrofitted Photocopier, Crocodile Clips,
TWO Dangerous Halogen Lamps & a Decommissioned Barcode Reader**

Valentine's Day

Dog Food Dinner Challenge

Inc. THREE FIVE STAR CHEFS & FOUR FIVE STAR TWATS off the TV

One-Tin Recipes Only

Sponsored by River Cottage, River Island & Pedigree Chum

—

BLIND AUCTION / BULK SALE / JOB LOT

Everything Must Go

Ninety Nine Thousand Portraits Of Hosni Mubarak Wearing Different Expressions Of A Benevolent Dictator

Inc. 'Oil Paintings' in Gold Frames, Official Photos, Posters, Murals & Nice Little Pictures For a Wall of an Office etc.
the Man Depicted in Various Postures & Locations by Sundry Different Portraitists
Buyer must collect from Egypt

See also other Job Lot of Old Portraits feat. Stalin, Ben Ali etc.
Special Offer: Statues of Saddam Hussein etc.

GENUINE ENQUIRIES ONLY. NO TIMEWASTERS.

February 15 2011

PURE CAPITAL
The Whole of Human Life Finally &
Emphatically Crystallised
Into A Digital / Financial Abstraction

No Flesh. No Soul. No Hope. No Charge for Admission. No Exit.

—

NARROWING PLANET
THE ABSOLUT BEST OF
WORLD MUSIC

Sponsored by Smirnoff

**CULTURES HAND PICKED & INDIVIDUALLY MASSACRED
BY SENSITIVE MUSICIAN TYPES Inc. STING & etc.**

—

IN THE BASEMENT (ADULTS ONLY)
Katie Price Has A Facial Hysterectomy

PLUS

Pointless Interrogation of a Minor Terror Suspect (12 Hours. No Interval.)

Moderate to Severe Upper Limb Viscosity

—

All England 'Ballad of Immense Suffering' Contest
Win the Holiday of a Lifetime for Nine

Beauty Contests
Miss Housing Benefit, Miss ASBO, Miss Grievous Bodily Harm.

Sour Face Bitches & Hard Nosed Bastards Contest
This Week
Ball Breakers vs Wife Beaters

Gruesome Video Footage
From The Reconstructed Cavern Club

Working For Murdoch
A FACT CHECKERS NIGHTMARE
£2.50 an hour

Apple Mac Assembly Workshop
Under 9s & Chinese Only. No Unions.

Celeb-Divorce Squash Court
feat. Racially Mixed Doubles
FREE ICE CREAM FOR THE PLAINTIFF

GRAND PUBLIC SPEAKING CONTEST

Holocaust Deniers

vs

Climate Change Deniers

KIDS WEARING TOO MUCH MAKE UP

VS

GROWN UPS WEARING TOO MUCH PERFUME

'Moderate' Racists

VS

White Supremacists

—

Opera For Which The Libretto is a Transcript of a Frantic 3am Conference Phone Call Between Leaders of Bahrain, Yemen, Libya & Iran

NO TRANSLATION
Music by Andrew Lloyd Webber & Bono
In Collaboration with Members of Take That

Jugglers Cooked in a Sauce of Asparagus & Strychnine

—

Forests That Are For Sale
& Then Not For Sale

—

A Workshop / Masterclass by Assorted Beggars

Inc.: How to LIVE on THREE EURO a day

Where to Sleep in the Metro

SIX new Approaches to Public Urination

—

An Ostrich & a Black Horse Tangled in Barbed Wire

—

A Symphony of Sound Bombs

May '68 at EURODISNEY

(Fancy Dress Contest / Costume Parade)

—

A Philosophical Discussion Whose Parameters Are Completely Unclear

PLUS

on TWO BROKEN BENCHES in a nearby square
(exact location to be DETERMINED): "THE ALCOHOLICS DEBATING CLUB"

—

Continuous Round-the-Clock Movie Screenings
WAY OF THE LOST (18 Cert)
RHETORIC OF THE LOST (15 Cert)
BENEATH THE PLANET OF THE LOST (PG)

—

Service Industry 'WANNABES' FIGHT NIGHT Special

Personal Assistants
vs
Personal Trainers

Winner Takes 'ALL'. Free H1N1 Vaccination for All Participants.

TUNNEL OF BLOOD
TUNNEL OF MUD
TUNNEL OF BONES
TUNNEL OF FLAME
WALL OF FLAME
WALL OF FEAR
WALL OF DEATH
WALL OF FIRE
WHEEL OF FIRE
WHEEL OF DOOM
WHEEL OF MISFORTUNE

PLUS other TUNNELS, WALLS & WHEELS t.b.c.
NO REFUNDS. BRING A BOTTLE.

February 21 2011

**Bahrain's Crown Prince
Sheikh Salman bin Hamad al-Khalifa
&
Leader of Libya
Colonel Muammar Gaddafi**

present

EXPLAINING JUSTICE TO A DEAD PROTESTOR

Performance Art Event / Pan Arab Double Act

(After Joseph Beuys)

Free Admission
Absolutely No Exit

Sponsored by Sandhurst
Aircraft, Cannons, Assault rifles, Shotguns, Sniper rifles & Submachine Guns
c/o UK Export Credits Guarantee Department

BOB SPATULA'S
HEAD INJURY MARATHON

All Proceeds To Charity

—

QUICK & EASY
LONG-SLEEVE
TO
SHORT-SLEEVE
SHIRT CONVERSION

Shirts Converted While You Wait
One-Way Only. No Refunds.

—

David 'Diplomat' Cameron
Double Purpose Democracy & Arms Trade Roadshow

Bulk Order Ballot Boxes – Get Rubber Bullets Free
All Fucking Manner of Hypocrites Welcome

—

Gaddafi Re-sets Standards to a New & Hideous Low
Follow Link To Buy Copy of His Stylish Umbrella

Grime Merchants on Ecstasy

Spectacular in Song, Dance, Mime & Striptease

NOW WITH BAFTA NOMINATED RELEVANCE & MULTIRACIAL CAST

PLUS

LARGELY OUTDATED SEMI-POLITICAL THEATRE WITH LIGHTING EXPERIMENTS FROM POLAND

Not Suitable for Michael Billington

—

From Tripoli

A DICTATOR WITH DEMENTIA WHOSE NAME IS DIFFICULT TO SPELL
RECOUNTS VIVID INCOMPREHENSIBLE NIGHTMARES:
Inc. CATS, RATS, MICE, DOGS & RODENTS
RISE UP & TAKE OVER LIBYA

Population Advised to Take Shelter

—

Israel Without Borders

David Cameron Without Proper Qualifications

Berlusconi Without Morals, Underpants or Trousers

"Carnival of the Mercenaries"
feat. Music by a DJ THAT WILL NOT PLAY REQUESTS

—

In The Basement
Bob Diamond Does 'Community Service'
The Original 'Mr. 1%' Teaches
Tax Avoidance For Proles

—

A Haemophilia of Tears

—

Social Networking for Jihadists
"Get the Most From your Facebook"

free concert

INAUDIBLE PEACE MUSIC FROM OUTER SPACE

—

Televised Assurances
Monotonous Goodwill*

*Now with Aspartame

—

PRO CELEBRITY TRANSPLANT BOXING

The Brain of Charlton Heston (Deceased) implanted in the body of Tiger Woods

VS

The Fists of Bruce Lee (Deceased) Surgically Co-mingled with the Arms of Hulk Hogan
Transplanted onto the FULLY FUNCTIONING Torso & Legs of Theo Walcott

(Winner Stays On. Loser Jumps Out of a Helicopter Over the Sahara without Parachute).

AUSTERITY FOREVER

PLUS

STACCATO DEATH THREATS BY TELEPHONE /
MONOLOGUES FROM MEN WHO MAY NOT BE ALIVE

set to hitherto undiscovered music
by Ahmed Fakroun
&
Indie 'Sensations' from Bosnia
The Precipice Calculator

—

A Dream In Which Your Legs Won't Move

—

Wisconsin Democrats
Sing the BEST of
Woody Guthrie

Secret Concert: Location to be Confirmed

Hilarious Prank Calls of a Teenage Genius
"The True Wit Of Telephonic Style"
Inc. "Do you do liver?", "I. M. A. GAY" & "Mr. C. My Balls"
& Other CLASSICAL PHONE GAGS OF THE MODERN ERA

—

World Leaders
Men vs Women
Pissing Contest

Dmitry Medvedev (Russia)
vs
Angela Merkel (Germany)

Jadranka Kosor (Croatia)
vs
Mahmoud Ahmadinejad (Iran)

George Papandreou (Greece)
vs
Julia Gillard (Australia)

& Special Novelty Match
Ban Ki-moon vs David Cameron & Nick Clegg (Coalition Entry)
Winner(s) Stay(s) On. Men with an Erection are DISQUALIFIED.

—

Cut & Paste Doctorates While U Wait
PHD Masterclass
with
'Dr.' Karl-Theodor zu Googleberg

Air Rifle Sniper Challenge

Target: ASHLEY COLE

Interns & Work Experience / 21s & Under Only

—

'ART' CINEMA SPECIAL
**Pina Bausch Claymation Tribute
by Aardman / Pixar & Wenders**

Best of the Internet #9

Pranks, Tricks & 'Accidents' with Superglue

Inc. Man with Fingers Glued to Penis, Man Glued to Toilet, Cat Glued to Car Roof, £1 glued to Paving Slabs & etc.

—

PHONE HACKING FOR 'JOURNALISTS'

—

De-Skilled Actors Workshop

present
Near-Nude Latin & Partly Bi-Sexual Burlesque

QUANDO QUANDO QUANGOS AGOGO

PLUS
From The Other Side of The World
The Incomprehensible Sensation
Hullapolloi

—

Official 'State-Sponsored'

Militarised Freedom March*

Starts 7am Prompt. No Latecomers. Black Tie & Black Shirts.
*Walk in time with the music or face the consequences.

Retro Talent Show

NEW FAECES

feat. A Man Who Can Blow Up A Balloon Using His Asshole,
Two Anorexic Triplets That Cannot Sing,
The Worlds Best & Only Comic Anaesthetist,
Dogs That Think They Are Cats etc.

PLUS

RAPID OVERFLOW

A Long Boring Opera

Depicting Statistical Detail of an Escalating Humanitarian Crisis On The Borders of Libya, Tunisia & Egypt

With Experimental Music by Ralph Intestine & Glandular Fever
Set Design by Zara Hadidi (sic) & Costumes by John Galliano
Sung by Luciano Pavarotti (Deceased) & 'TWO LIVING TENORS'
WITH a chorus of 140,000 extras
Directed by António Guterres UN High Commissioner for Refugees in Collaboration with Muammar Gaddafi

TOUGH LOVE
TOUGH LUCK
TOUGH TIMES
TOUGH TALK
TOUGH JUSTICE
TOUGH SHIT
TOUGH MEDICINE
ROUGH BREAKS
ROUGH LANGUAGE
ROUGH TREATMENT

—

In The Basement
Drs. Mortise & Tenon
HIP REPLACEMENTS WHILE–U–WAIT*
*discount for patients who bring their own knives

NON-CONSENSUAL FACEPAINTING

Sponsored by Dulux, Whitewash & Humbrol

—

'THE GREAT DEBATE'

Men With Intellectual Diphtheria
VS
Women With Philosophical Typhoid

—

In The Foyer

A Duet For Tape Recorder, Tambourine & Bass
Celebrating Recent Achievements
of The British Nation

Sung by Petra Von Borgen, Amisha Patel & Colleen Handy

ABSOLUTELY
NO FOREIGNERS

International PR / Marketing Challenge

Re-Branding Gaddafi

**First Prize: Penthouse Villa in Zawiyah
& LIFETIME SUPPLY OF TEAR GAS
Second Prize: Free Tix for a Concert by Mariah Carey**

PLUS

In The Bathroom of The Beverly Hilton

Charlie Sheen & His Amazing Technicolour Dreamcoke

—

Talks Event:
Miss World 1930 INTERVIEWS Miss World 2011

—

Members of the Upper Class will say Sorry for What They Have Done

Cirque du Drunk

Stomach Pumpers Sans Safety Net

—

Foyer Events:

Downward Spiral of a Federal Reserve

Crashing Prices & Runs on a Well Known Bank

—

Rogue Traders

(solo performance)

—

Celebrititis (Three Day Cure)

—

Basement Closed for Rapid Refurbishment

Live by WEBCAM

THE COMPLETE & UNEXPURGATED SOLITARY CONFINEMENT OF PRIVATE BRADLEY MANNING

Set to Horrible Slowed Down Music
by a Certain 'Wolfgang Amadeus Mozart' (Deceased)

Set Design by Quantico. Feat. Torture, Nudity, Abuse & Bad Language.

PLUS

Trade Mission to Benghazi

Top Secret Undercover SAS / MI6 Tactical Sales Booth CANCELLED

—

In Concert
Fearful, Downcast & Joyless People

Dogs Fighting in Fog

(Various Sizes. Most Dogs Gray Coloured).

—

SHROVE TUESDAY SPECIAL

Pre-Adulterated PANCAKES
Inc. Free Fruit Substitute
& 14 Experimental Additives

Endorsed by a Man that Once Played Doctors & Nurses with Jamie Oliver's Wife

PLUS

Sandwiches with Sand as Ingredient

—

PERISTALSIS: THE OPERA
SLOW MOTION BOWEL MOVEMENTS
OF A FORMER COMMUNIST

Inevitable Disappointment
&
General Disfigurement

—

5
UNDERAGE
& TECHNICALLY
NAKED
GIRLS

In a Room Equidistant from The Houses of Parliament
& Buckingham Palace

—

Debate-a-Thong

Politicians of Various Persuasions
With a Strange Facial Rictus

vs

Spokesmodels for Haliburton / Xe

Thongs Designed by Victoria Beckham. Topics Selected at Random. Winners Stay On.
Top Prize: Bucket of Whisky

Experimental Franglais Choreography

L'Après Midi Des International Landmine Victims

Probably Not Suitable for Children

—

ALL NUDE Ritual & FULLY Public

Disability & Fitness-For-Work Testing

Sponsored by Coalition 'Govt'.

Inc. Big Society Egg & Spoon Race,
Progressive Incontinence Challenge,
Greasy Pole of Fairness,
Very Greasy Pole of Opportunity etc.

—

Scary Blokes IN A RENTAL CAR

Free Speech for Poisoners

THE COMPLETE PRIVATISATION OF EVERYTHING

—

Spineless Leaders & Followers With No Backbone

LOOK MA "NO STRINGS"
Non-Independent Conference of Political Puppets

feat. Tedious & Shameful Opening Speech by Charismatic Clegg

PLUS

Disguising Cluelessness (Workshop)

&

Holographic Morality (Lib Dem Mime Show)

Animals Launched into Another Dimension for Purposes of a Scientific Experiment

Inc.

Donkeys, Chimps, Spiders, Dolphins, Flies etc.

plus

COOLING PROBLEMS

New Nuclear Comedy from Japan

—

SALE ITEMS

Olde Fashioned Euro WAG Makeovers by Messrs. Verdant, Viceroy & Pomegranate

Parisian Wet Suits

Libyan Freedom

—

In The Café

EATING AS STARVATION

ALL NEW
NAKED
ENNUI-CAMS

—

TOP TEN BEST
TSUNAMI MEDICINES

—

IN THE CAR PARK
"ANY WILLING PROVIDER"

presents

AMATEUR NOSE JOBS
PERFORMED WITH A SPADE
INSTEAD OF A SCALPEL
& ALCOPOPS
INSTEAD OF ANAESTHETIC

Royal Wedding Live
1:25 Scale

Complete & Comprehensive
Pre-Event Pre-Enactment

**Feat. Look-a-Like Dwarves,
Mimicking Midgets & Copy-Cat Children**

Tickets 500 Guineas
Limited Number of Free Places for People in Wheelchairs

Free Bottle of Top Quality Asti Spumante. Sponsored by Grazia.

—

A Savage Pre-Dawn Assault by Loyalist Government Riot Police

Sky Black Like The End Of The World

School Children From All Over The World
present

An Ambitious Dance
Depicting the Complicated Emergency Operations
to Pump Seawater into the Crippled Reactors
at Fukushima Daiichi Nuclear Power Station

Not Suitable for Children

PLUS

**Powerful Post–Women's Day 'Think Piece'
feat. Diana Princess of Wales (deceased)
in conversation with Liz Hurley's Breasts**

—

Lawyers, Tories, City Analysts & Futures Traders
Sent to the Countryside for
Compulsory RE-EDUCATION by Bumpkins

March 16 2011

Gallows Humour From Libya

BYE BYE BENGHAZI

—

The MIGHTY, HIGH MINDED & IMPOTENT TALKING SHOP
of
THE UNITED NATIONS
presents

"NO FLY ZONE
In a Restaurant Kitchen"

PLUS

A CONCERT FOR JAPAN

Collaboration by the Chernobyl Orchestra & the Harrisburg String Quartet

"GEIGER COUNTER SYMPHONY"

Music by John Cage / Kraftwerk. Narrated by Sir Peter Ustinov (C.B.E.) (Deceased).

Wall of Science
Wall of Silence
Wall of Debt
Wall of Acrimony
Wall of Deception
Wall of Water
Wall of Blood

Plus Other Walls t.b.c.

ALL NEW

ONTOLOGICAL DISTURBANCES OF THE WESTERN HEMISPHERE

—

In the annex
POST ST. PATRICK'S DAY "BREAKFAST HANGOVER CLUB"

Discounted admission for Irish, Wannabes & General Hangers-on.
Free 'Hilarious Green-Coloured Outsized Shamrock / Leprechaun Hat'
Filled With Tea, Potatoes, Beer, Sausage & Kebab Vomit

PLUS

Fukushima Power Station
HUMANITARIAN HIGH ALTITUDE
INTERNATIONAL CHARITY PISSING CONTEST

HELP COOL THE REACTORS

Longest Urination Wins A Prize from TEPCO / NISA. Judges' Decision is Final.
Contestants Must Bring Own Food, Drinking Water & Radiation Suits
Helicopter Provided

The Fingers of a Thief
Crushed
Using His Own
Concrete

—

Men In Women's Clothing

Investigative Journalists in the back of a Sponsored Military Truck

—

HOMELESS HULA-HOOPING CONTEST
Vagrants Compete For 'A Safe Place To Sleep'

First Prize: 8 Nights in a Hotel Room where the Air is 98% Air Freshener & 23% Bleach

Cruel & Usual Punishment

PLUS

MORONIC BEER TENT

&

"Donkey Meat Sandwiches"

—

OUTSIDE EVENT

**Sad Looking English Girls
Swim Topless
in a Lake of Tears**

Prize Certificates for all Participants
presented by Mich Hucknell (sic) & Jimmy Savile O.B.E.

SIX Famous Public Buildings Filled With Water

(Inc. Tower of London, Pompidou, Eiffel Tower, White House, etc.)

—

First Day of Spring

**Playgrounds TAKEN OVER
by Homeless Junkies**

**Public Buildings Closed then
TURNED into LUXURY Apartments**

—

In the Basement

ALL NUDE GIRLS of BERLUSCONI
Present

"Daddy: A Musical Revue"

with Songs by a Man that does Musical Farts

Women Who Are Out of Touch Argue with Men Who Are Out of Time

—

World Leaders Scary Fucking Staring Contest

The All Time RECORD Holder

Lady Margaret Thatcher 'Former Prime Minister of England' etc.

VS

The CHALLENGER

ALL the WAY from Iran

Mr. Mahmoud 'The Vote Rigger' Ahmadinejad

—

Ice Cream in a Variety of Flavours
Inspired by the Bombing of Libya

Nightly Bombardment*

*Twice on Sundays

—

BUDGET SPECIAL

Inflation: The Musical

Directed by Osborne. Script by A. Smith. Music by Privilege, Wanker & Cacophony. Ticket Prices Subject to Change. May Contain Index-Linked Strobe Lighting & Traces of Shit.

Not Suitable For Sick People or Paupers

—

In The Annex

Genetically Modified Arm Wrestling

Bob 'the Octopus' Brown
vs
Karl 'the Monkey Man' Malone

ALL HUMAN POVERTY Completely & Irreversibly ERASED Through A Manipulation of the Statistics as CYNICAL as it is DEVIOUS, CONNIVING & MATHEMATICALLY DUBIOUS

—

"DRAMATISED MEMORIES OF SIR RICHARD BURTON"

ELIZABETH TAYLOR (DECEASED) AS CLEOPATRA (DECEASED)

—

BLUES EXPLOSION FROM BOSNIA
REGGAE SUNBURN FROM GAZA
SKIFFLE FROM HELL

ALL PURPOSE EMPTINESS

SHARP PAIN, SCATTERED CLOUDS & DULL UBIQUITOUS ACHES

—

COMPLICATED, DYSFUNCTIONAL
& ECONOMICALLY MOTIVATED
MERGERS OF HOSPITALS, PRISONS,
NURSERY SCHOOLS & MENTAL ASYLUMS

—

CELEBRITY CHEMOTHERAPY (MINI-SERIES)
TRANQUILISING THE UNDER 5s (WORKSHOP)
HOW TO SPIT FURTHER (9-PART 6-HOUR MASTERCLASS)
AIRSTRIKES FOR DEMOCRACY (etc.)

—

BLOOD & GUTS IN TECHNICOLOUR

GROWING CRACKS
IN THE FUKISHIMA REACTOR CORE

REPRESENTED

IN A BUTOH DANCE THAT IS TROUBLING & MYSTERIOUS

Sponsored by The Mail on Sunday Times
Music by Victoria Beckham & Sheryl Gascoigne

WINDS LIGHT TO MODERATE & BLOWING IN THE DIRECTION OF LOS ANGELES

—

URBAN WARFARE
FREESTYLE
DEATHMATCH CHALLENGE

BEST OF US ARMY AFGHANISTAN KILL TEAMS
vs
PRO-GADDAFI LOYALIST SNIPERS

TRANSGENDER RAMBO IMPERSONATORS
vs
CROSSDRESSING TERMINATOR IMPERSONATORS

1970s PROVOS
vs
1980s HIZBULLAH

"Winner Stays On"

Trauma 45
MEGA MIX

Medley of 600,000
Genuinely Upsetting Songs

Inc. Bright Eyes, Send in the Clowns, Paddy McGinty's Goat etc.

Extra Strings by Andre Previn & Jacqueline du Pré
Sponsored by Golden Syrup & Kleenex

—

POETRY READING

Nick Clegg: Lamentations of a Liar

&

Ode to a Nightsight Rifle
Lyrical Advertisement. Adapted from a poem by Keats.
feat. High Spec X26 Thermal Weapon Scope
Guaranteed Lowest Retail Price

BREATH HOLDING CONTEST
"WHO CAN LAST LONGEST IN A FORD FOCUS FILLED ENTIRELY WITH PETROL?"

FEAT. 6.3 TYPICAL WHITE FAMILIES FROM 'ALARM CLOCK BRITAIN'

—

The Institutional Production of Stupidity Dumbness & Idiocy

—

FREEDOM PICNIC AT FORTNUM & MASON

FREE ADMISSION
Sponsored by Harrods. Free Fragrance samples by Tommy Hilfiger.

ALARM COCK BRITAIN

starring

JEREMY CUNT

& OTHER SPOONERISTIC / TYPO BREAKFAST PORN

—

Asymmetrical Warfare: A Balanced View

Presented by Paxman, Limbaugh, O'Reilly & Snow

—

SPECIAL LATE NIGHT ALL EUROPE (UK FINALS)

"CIRCUS ANIMAL KICKING CONTEST"
This Week: Elephants

Next Week: Zoo Animal Kicking Contest feat. "Knut & Friends"

SPONSORED BY DOC. MARTENS
& WELLINGTON BOOT & Co.

Interval Music by Nancy Sinatra

ADVANCED USELESSNESS

Training for Juvenile Idiots / Retraining for Decrepit Fools

—

'Armagideon Time'

ARTISTS ONLY HIGH CULTURE BUNGA BUNGA

BEAUTY CONTEST

Prizes Presented by Royal Opera House & Nice-Looking-Deep-Voice-Bloke off the Telly
Results Announced by a MODERNISED TELEGRAM. Judges Decision is Final.

PLUS

Grinding Poverty, Corruption, Unemployment & Police Abuses
NOW with ADDITIONAL WATER CANNONS

—

"God Save The Queen" etc.

Starring 'England' as an intolerant & intolerable cesspool

SHIT FINDS ITS OWN LEVEL

'Free' Market as a FORM of DEMOCRACY

'Warts & All Reactor Core Tour'

CANCELLED DUE TO TOTAL LACK OF FUNDING

—

IN THE BASEMENT

A MASSIVE MACHINERY OF REPRESSION,
CONTROL & SUBJUGATION
DECORATED WITH FLAGS, BALLOONS
& HOMEMADE BUNTING

OUTSIDE

Asstd. Directors & Managers of Arts Organisations Perform Pathetic Pseudo-Victorian Dances of Faux Gratitude
Fawning, Bowing, Slobbering & Scraping the Cobblestones With Their Filthy Caps
as Tourists Look On in Delight, Throwing Coins at the Capering Artists
'Gawd Bless Yew All Kinde Genlemen, We Are Evrr, Evver So Gwateful for Yr Patronage'
& etc.

CANCELLED DUE TO TOTAL LACK OF INTEREST

—

BASEMENT SEMINAR

Compensation Advice Session

APRIL FOOLS DAY & THE LAW

Inc. How to CLAIM for Prank-Induced Injury, Blinding, Humiliation, Trauma, Shock, Ridicule & Emotional Distress

NO WIN. NO FEE.

Retrospective Claims from Childhood a Speciality

CANCELLED DUE TO TOTAL LACK OF ENTHUSIASM

—

BOOK BURNING FOR BEGINNERS (WORKSHOP)

Led by US pastor Terry Jones & Friends
feat. Inspiring Examples from History Inc. The Nazis & Khmer Rouge

—

In The Car Park

VERY TALL DANCING GIRLS ON HIGH SPEED ROTATING PODIUMS

CANCELLED DUE TO TOTAL LACK OF ENERGY

—

"Ye Streetz ov LNDN"

True But Hackneyed Tales of Everyday Hackney

Written by Bob Dickensian. Directed by Ray Winstone
Dances by The Ballet Boyz

Starring: Some Lass From EastEnders & A Bloke That Once Thumped Sean Meadows
& Introducing Gratuitous Bisexual Love Interest

PLUS

Interactive Tedium

8-Late. Anybody Welcome.

CANCELLED DUE TO UNEXPECTED TECHNICAL DIFFICULTIES

—

Bizet's Undiscovered & Supposedly Controversial All NUDE Masterwork

"Life in The Economic Slow Lane"

AN ALLEGORICAL OPERA ABOUT A GOVERNMENT OF MEAN SELF-SATISFIED DRUNKS, PRIGGS & PIGS
PRESIDING OVER A NATION OF SMALL MINDED BALDING / PREMATURELY MENOPAUSAL BIGOTS

PLUS

MOB RULE FOR LONDON
(SUBJECT TO REFERENDUM)

Belly Dancers in Quicksand
Buskers in Aspic
Rottweilers in a Pub Car Park
Radioactive Isotopes in Highly Corrosive Sea Water

—

A Great Leap Forward In The Annex

REPRESENTATIVES OF THE CHINESE AUTHORITIES PRESENT

"DISSIDENT ARTISTS FREE PRISON STUDIO PROGRAMME"

—

Monarchist Theatre of Dramatic Reconstruction
Royal Wedding Countdown Special

The Posthumous Re-Execution of Oliver Cromwell (Deceased)

Starring a Very Distant Unproven Relation of the Original Gentleman

PLUS

SIX GREAT SPEECHES BY POLITICIANS ON PROZAC

**THE KINDS OF CORRIDORS
THAT MAKE PEOPLE THINK OF FIREBALLS**

**THE KINDS OF STAIRWELLS
THAT MAKE PEOPLE THINK OF A BUILDING'S COLLAPSE**

—

BEST OF LONDON TRANSPORT CCTV

#1 Bodily Functions & Malfunctions

feat.
FAT MAN SHITTING ON AN ESCALATOR
TWO TARTS PISSING IN A HARRODS BAG
"EPILEPTIC ELEVATOR"
BACK OF THE BUS BLOW JOB PLUS NOSEBLEED
'PASSENGER ACTION' AT LEICESTER SQUARE

Soundtrack by MC Butterfingers & DJ Rent-a-Mouth

—

COPS IN THE DOCK
with very special guest
PC SIMON HARWOOD

EVERYTHING MUST GO FORECLOSURE SALE:

PORTUGAL

—

SELF DELUSION MASTERCLASS

Sessions With Top International Experts
Inc. M. Carey, 'Dave' Cameron, Laim (sic) Gallagher, M. Zuckerberg, Laurent Gbagbo & Lily Allen
SPECIAL LECTURE: Tony Blair

—

New Epistolatory Drama from Libya
Love Letters to Obama
by M. Gaddafi

—

RECIPES FROM THE AUSTERITY COOKBOOK

by 'Greek Chefs', Nick, Nicky & Nickos Colostomy
Refried & Regurgitated Radioactive Hamburger Residue
Broiled Shoe & Defoliated Grass Shavings Served on a Polenta of Styrofoam
Pasta Pesto Pauper-Style

WORKSHOP
for
MANAGERS

HIDING YOUR BONUS
CONCEALING THE SIZE OF YOUR BONUS
BONUS OBFUSCATION
CREATIVE BONUS ACCOUNTING
BONUS-LYING BY OMISSION
PLUS
SACKING AN INFERIOR WORKER

—

LATE NIGHT CABARET
Sponsored by Haliburton & British Aeronautics

A Man Who is Paralysed

in All PARTS except for HIS PENIS

Plays the Xylophone

& Sends ELABORATE Text Messages

to Members of the Audience

—

IN THE CAR PARK
ENGLAND STIRS SLIGHTLY
THEN GOES BACK TO SLEEP

Staring Contest

Politicians

vs

Religious Zealots

Economic Commentators of All Persuasions

vs

Recently Lobotomised Patients of A Mental Institution

etc.

Winner stays ON

Also participating: Method Actors, Post Traumatic Stress Patients, Intellectual Half-Wits, Kids on Heavy Sedatives, Junkies, TV analysts, Semi-Professional Goalkeepers, Petrified Rodents etc.

—

In the Car Park

'CRY BABY CLEGG' THE HUMAN PUNCHBAG

Three Punches for £5. Five Kicks for £4. Six Punches for £2.
Free Kicks for Bank Interns & Recently Sanctioned Welfare Claimants

Knock Him Over – Win a Holiday

ABSOLUTELY No Entry for People From SHEFFIELD

INTERNATIONAL GUN RAMPAGE LOCATION FREESTYLE

Inc. Shopping Malls, Nuclear Submarines, Suburban Teen Parties, Schools etc.

PLUS

Genetically Modified

DISH OF THE DAY

"Lamb Tentacles served in a sauce of Crab Cheese & Quail Testicles"

Cocktail of the Week
"American Shutdown"

—

THORNS IN THE EYES OF A POLYMATH

Educational Drama from England
ALL TICKETS £9,000. Increased Access for All. No Proles. No 'Minorities'.

—

In the Cellar
Private Show

All New Adventures of MISS WHIPLASH

Not Suitable for People Who've Been in Car Accidents

All Day Special / Vacuum Days 'Centenary Plus One'

101 Miserable Sensations

Including:

General Malaise of Shopping Mall
Supremacy of Guns vs Words
Sadness at Gut Cancer Clinic
All Purpose History of Greed
Headaches & Spontaneous Blindness
Hope Drowned in a Bucket of Lies
Last Dance at Morbid PowerPoint Disco
Constipation of a Trade Unionist
Pancakes 'Quatre Merde'
Semi-Professional Child Abuse
Vague Rambling of Man Outside an Off Licence
Scattered Showers & General Desolation
Sound of Wind Howling Through The London Eye
Shit Seeping Through a Broken Down Wall
Internalised Advertising
Malicious Assortment of Capitalist Vortices
Radioactive Internet
Thorn in the Eyes of a Beholder
Slumped Market / Cancelled Bus Lane
Triple Amputation
Logic Problems / Operational Difficulties
Promiscuous Grandparents

PLUS OTHER SENSATIONS t.b.c.

Politically Correct Wrestling

Non-White Asian / Other / Roma-Anglo Males

VS

Other British Mixed White Transgender Self–Identified Women

PLUS ALL NEW TAG-TEAM BARE-KNUCKLE GRUDGE-MATCH

Men Who Couldn't Care Less

VS

Women Who Care Too Much

—

LIFE AFFIRMING MUSIC BY DOLPHINS INSPIRED BY THE WISDOM OF CALIFORNIAN MORONS

feat. CRYSTAL LIGHTSHOW & 'FREE' LUCID DREAMING TAXATION ADVICE

GUEST APPEARANCES BY CHER, WAYNE ROONEY & PETER MANDERLSON (sic)

Nick Clegg

TEARS OF A CLOWN/ CRY ME A RIVER

Nine-Hour Solo of Gutless Weeping
feat. Sad Tunes off Radio Three
& That One They Used in the Choc Ice Ad
"Choreography by Nelly Futardedo (Sic)"

GUARANTEED: ALL OBFUSCATING HUMAN INTEREST & NO POLITICS

OR YOUR MONEY BACK

PLUS

**ALL NEW ADVENTURES
OF MAN WITH HEAD STUCK IN A BUCKET
Not Suitable for Claustrophobes or Window Cleaners**

—

A CRISIS IN REPRESENTATION /
STERLING DOWN BY SEVERAL POINTS AGAINST THE YEN

"HAVE A NICE DAY"
"KEEP IT REAL"

New System of Government Powered Entirely by Hot Air

—

CAMERON & LANSLEY

present

COCK UPS
A Sexy Spending Revue

(a.k.a. "Front Line Services / Big Tits of NHS")

feat. All Nude Ex-Nurses & Re-Trained Morgue Attendants

Dance of the Former Anaesthetists etc.

—

AUSTERITY BREAKFAST
ONE PER FAMILY

Stale Bread Soaked in Vinegar Substitute

Salt on Toasted Partially Recycled Newsprint

Deep Fried Metal Scraps

—

Breathless Enthusiasm of Gormless New Media Gurus

Twitter for the Dead

In Womb Web 2.0

& etc.

BEST OF A&E / EMERGENCY ROOM CCTV

#1 Drunk Fights

Men With Broken Legs

vs

Man in Wheelchair

Man in Neck Brace

vs

Woman in a Coma

White Teens Covered in Blood

vs

Black Teens Covered in Talcum Powder

—

Burqa Ban

Crucifix Ban

Flip Flops & Ugg Boots Ban

Long Flappy Cardigan Ban

Nike Ban

Plus Other Bans t.b.c.

Faith Schools Science Departments

100% Accurate
Reconstruction of Norah's Ark (sic)

Inc. Animals in Exact Alphabetical Order that God Intended Historically

PLUS

Richard Dawkins
Conversion Challenge

Religious Zealots of all Kinds
Attempt to Persuade the Principled Atheist
of their Very Own One True Way
24 Hour Time Limit. Intellectual & Spiritual Guidance Only.
No Torture. No Blackmail. No Bribery.
No Scientologists

—

Climate Change Sceptics Heated 'til They Boil

Eurosceptics Made to Walk The Channel Tunnel

General Sceptics Subjected to General Anaesthetic

PRE-OLYMPIC SPECIAL

'Threshold of Pain'

Which Sports Personalities can take the most Voltage?

—

The Karma Sutra of Torture

Based on Texts by CIA / White Homeland Commando Unit / MI5 / MI6 / GESTAPO & MOSSAD

—

Fist Fight: Celebrity Hangers-On vs Paparazzi

—

Concert of New Music from Stereophonics
Inspired by the deteriorating situation in Helmand Province of Afghanistan
PLUS experimental / malfunctioning AutoCAD visuals by a total tosser

ALL THE BAD FEELING IN ENGLAND

EXTRACTED IN AN ALCHEMICAL / INDUSTRIAL PROCESS
TURNED INTO A STRANGE ROCK-LIKE SUBSTANCE
GROUND DOWN TO A FINE POWDER
SHIPPED OUT ON BARGES & TIPPED INTO THE CHANNEL

—

Lancôme
'Eau de Desperation'

—

COMPULSORY
PRONUNCIATION LESSONS

al-Qaeda (a.k.a. al-Qaida, al-Qa'ida etc.

ALL NUDE Bacteria
of the Playboy Mansion Hot Tub

—

"You Can Cut a Deal With Me..."
Interrogational Arabic (Intermediate Level)

Lesson Twelve: Good Cop / Bad Cop
Lesson Thirteen: We've been watching you for months
Lesson Fourteen: Your friend confessed already
Lesson Fifteen: Suck My Truncheon Sand Monkey

—

COMPLICATED VOTES
ABOUT VOTES

'FIRST PAST THE POST'
VS
'WINNER STAYS ON'
VS
'COME IN MOUTH'
VS
'NEOLIBERAL DICTATORSHIP'
VS
'OBSESSIVE–COMPULSIVE BRAINWASH'
VS
'IDIOTIC MONARCHY'

THE SLUMP OF THE U.S. DEBT RATING
from Standard & Poor
REPRESENTED BY A SINGLE SLOW DESCENDING NOTE
PLAYED BY A FORMER BLUE CHIP STOCKBROKER
ON A HIGHLY COLLECTIBLE BUT BADLY MADE VIOLIN

—

CABARET EVENING

Well Known Comics from Goldman Sachs Take The Piss Out of Everyone

Tickets $2.74bn in the first quarter

—

Interactive Gameshow from Croatia

National Outrage / 'Joint Criminal Enterprise'

Live from Hague. Win a Looted TV.
Hosted by Ante Gotovina & Mladen Markač
Theme tune by Ceca
Dubbed Laughter by Tudjman & Milošević

—

Cutting Edge Theatre

'New Mime from Fallujah'

'Best of Women's Writing from Helmand'

Product Launch

PHANTASMAGORICAL BREAKFAST CEREAL

Only 2 Calories per Serving. "100% of RDA"
With Live PA / Testimonial from a Dead Model
Inc. Photos by a bald Austrian bloke

—

Fashion Show of Clothes Designed by a recently rehabilitated Murderer

Barbeque Food from an Unconvicted Arsonist

IN CONCERT

'Doppelgangers of the Jackson 5'

—

al-Qaeda
OPEN EVENING

GET TO KNOW THE PEOPLE WHO WILL BE RUNNING YOUR COUNTRY

EVERYBODY WELCOME
Inc. All You Need to Know About SHARIA LAW
Free Crèche (Boys Only) / Weapons Training

Sponsored by Birmingham UKIP & The Daily Express

A MACHINE FOR TURNING TRAGEDY INTO ENTERTAINMENT

(PATENT PENDING)

Before operating the unit, please read the manual thoroughly & retain it for future reference.

Foyer Closed

Basement Closed

Theatre Closed

Annex Closed

—

Outdoor Events

Explosions of an Economic Underclass

Breast Enlargement for Beginners (Workshop)

Intolerance In General

DE-LEGALISATION OF THINGS THAT WERE OTHERWISE ALLOWED

Fist Fight

All New Restructured & Relocated
Part-Time Trainee Management Team

VS

Six Old Blokes from Accounting or Maintenance

Winner stays ON

Also participating: Non-Speaking Extras from Harry Potter, Hobbits etc. Kids from Dewsbury,
Blind Pensioners & 'Bonnie' Prince Harry

NO Kicking. NO Biting.

PLUS

Lunchtime Concert
on a stolen reconstructed replica Harpsichord

—

Dead Horses Flogged until their very Bones are Soup

ALL WEEK
In the Basement

ROYAL WEDDING SPECIAL
EXPERIMENTAL EXECUTIONS

#1 Charles & Camilla

Covered in Home Counties Honey,
Staked Out on the Number One Court at Wimbledon
& Left For The Crows

PLUS

#2 The Duchess & Duke of Gloucester

Drowned in A Vat of Shredded Flags & Bullshit

"Death to the Monarchy"*

*No Actual Treason Intended. Sponsored by Grazia.

—

Pre-emptive Precautionary Arrest of Seditious Persons
Inc. Schoolchildren, Bad Debtors & Pensioners with Political Opinions

Brutal Interrogation of People Planning Not to Go to a Stupid Streetparty
& Other Justifiable Measures to Keep The Population in Check t.b.c.

ALL WEEK
In the Basement

ROYAL WEDDING SPECIAL EXPERIMENTAL EXECUTIONS

#3 Prince Edward & Katherine (Duke & Duchess of Kent)

Hanged by the Neck Until Dead
Using Bunting & Raffia in Red, White & Blue
(Gibbet Lamp Posts Created by London's Finest Artisans)

PLUS

#4 Prince Michael of Kent

Boiled in Paupers' Blood then Fired from a Cannon at Dawn

—

Feeding Frenzy of the Tabloids

63 B-LIST CELEBRITIES
THROWN NAKED IN A POOL OF GREASED PAPARAZZI & ITINERANT PHONE HACKERS
First Celeb to Expire Gets a Posthumous Contract with Max Clifford

April 27 2011

ALL WEEK
In the Basement

ROYAL WEDDING SPECIAL EXPERIMENTAL EXECUTIONS

#5 Princess Michael of Kent

Hung Upside Down On A Meathook
from the Roof of a BP Petrol Station

—

#6 HIS ROYAL HIGHNESS PRINCE HARRY OF WALES

Thrown from the White Cliffs of Dover

—

#7 Princess Alexandra
The Horrible Lady Oglivy

SUSPENDED BY THE ANKLES FROM A MASSIVE BUNCH
OF UNION JACK HELIUM BALLOONS & CAUSED TO FLOAT AWAY

April 28 2011

ALL WEEK
ROYAL WEDDING SPECIAL

EXPERIMENTAL EXECUTIONS #8–15 inclusive: JOB-LOT THURSDAY BONANZA

'ABSOLUTELY NO IRONY INTENDED'

Anne, Princess Royal

Seen Off By A Firing Squad of Deaf, Dumb & Blind Old Etonians

Prince Andrew, Duke of York

Chopped Up by Gordon Ramsay & Fed To The Corgis

Sophie, Countess of Wessex

Stoned by a Mob of 'Modern-Day Peasants' Wearing Reeboks & Shell Suits
Who Darken the Sky with a Deadly Hail of Commemorative Cutlery, Coins, Cobblestones
& Crockery Strangely Reminiscent of the Battle Of Agincourt

Prince Edward, Earl of Wessex

Drowned in Collected Sweat of The Working Classes (sic)

Princess Beatrice of York
&
Princess Eugenie of York

Set Adrift on an Unseaworthy Craft Resembling the Raft of the Medusa
as Depicted by the French Romantic Painter & Lithographer Théodore Géricault,
& Accompanied by an Untrustworthy Crew of Manservants, Maids & Footmen

Princess Louise of Wessex a.k.a.
Lady Louise Windsor

Suffocated by the Breasts of Assorted 'Lads' Mag' Cover Girls. feat. Lucy Pinder & Barbara Windsor (Deceased)

Prince James of Wessex a.k.a. Viscount Severn

Wrapped in Street Party Banners, Weighted Down with Lead, Bricks, Pomp & Ceremony
& Cast from the VERY HIGHEST PINNACLE of Canary Wharf

FREE BEER & SAUSAGE SANDWICHES ON BREAD STAINED RED, WHITE & BLUE

LAST DAY
WEDDING WEEK SPECIAL: EXPERIMENTAL EXECUTIONS

EVERYTHING MUST GO

Her Majesty Queen Elizabeth II & Prince Philip, Duke of Edinburgh

DISPATCHED BY MEANS OF A HOMEMADE ELECTRIC CHAIR
DESIGNED & BUILT BY SCHOOLCHILDREN
REPRESENTING ALL NATIONS OF THE FORMER BRITISH COMMONWEALTH

PLUS

The Main Event

Prince William of Wales
& Kate Symbolic-Commoner Middleton

Asphyxiated Through Sheer Boredom
During a Lengthy, Complex & Tedious Historical Pageant

Also feat. Ronnie & Reggie Kray, Sir Elton John, Guy Ritchie, Arthur Askey,
Sir Francis Drake, Emily Brontë, Mrs. Beeton, Katie Price & Albert Pierrepoint & Co.
Directed by Peter Brook's Osteopath. Costumes by Vivienne Westwood
Music by Tinchy Stryder & The Choir Of Westminster Abbey

Pre-execution Interviews by Martin Bashir

No Interval

Photographs by The Two Davids (Bailey & Hamilton)
Refreshments Courtesy of Her Majesty's Prison Service Catering Department

FINALE

Participatory Theatre for Rooftop Snipers & 2,000 Wedding Guests

Dulce Et Decorum Est

Nothing Will Come of Nothing

Live Video Link-up from the Impotent Royal Marriage Bed of Shame

PLUS

Commentary by Royalist Sex Therapists

King in the Palace and What in the Bedroom?

Interval Concert by Lady Gaga

PLUS

A Giant Pipeline Carrying Dirty Oil From Canada to Texas

—

Pre-Emptive Trial of Activists that Were Previously Pre-Emptively Arrested
Plus Pre-Emptive Sentencing & Pre-Emptive Refusal of Remission
Increased Optimism for Non-Descript Brown-Haired Girls

Discount on Flags & Bunting

242,000 Big Screen Channels of Rhapsodic Patriotic Flatulence

—

Elsewhere
International Dominoes Continues
Uganda vs Syria
Next contestant: Ivory Coast

In the Car Park
Top Prizes. Win an iPod.

Death Plunge
Bungee Jump
Challenge

from the penultimate topmost PLATFORM of a Demolition Crane

"Who can LAND safely
in a Paddling Pool
Half Filled with Urine & 'Continental Lager'?"

(SORRY – NO UNDER 5s)

—

**The RIVER THAMES
dyed DAYGLO using SCIENTIFIC MATERIALS
in COLOURS that approximate
RED, ORANGE & DARK GREEN
the latter to make it more like a postcard,
the former for reasons that no one understands**

FREE MICROWAVE, TASTELESS DINNER & A KICK IN THE TEETH FOR ALL WORKERS OF THE WORLD

Genuine / Willing, QUALIFIED & Humble Workers Only

—

Dis-United Nations Convention of Ethical Contortionists

—

Syrian Snipers vs Unarmed Pedestrians

The Posthumous Speeches of Saif al-Arab Gaddafi
(Topics to be Announced)

HOUSE FOR SALE

Six metre (18ft) high perimeter walls topped with barbed wire
Three Storeys High. Few Windows (Mostly Opaque).
Third-floor terrace shielded by 'privacy wall'
Inc. 3,000 sq yard Compound
No Internet or Telephone connection

Two security gates

Access to the compound severely restricted
Abbottabad Western District, Pakistan
Convenient for Pakistan Military Academy, Golf Club & Parade Ground
Previous Occupant Deceased
Offers in the region of $1m (£600,000)

—

Walt Diserney (sic) presents

The Undersea Adventures of Osama Bin Laden

Suitable for Children & Mad Hatter's Tea Party

PLUS

AL-QAEDA LEADERSHIP NEW VACANCIES / RECRUITMENT DRIVE
No Women. No Jews. No Infidels.

'Operation Geronimo'
Boastful Americans Talk Shit About Democracy,
Whilst Confusing Vengeance with Justice

True Grit Remix / Strange Bedfellows
feat. Unexpected Love Poems by Glenn Beck to Barack Obama's Decisive Manhood
With Contributions by George W. Bush & Rush Limbaugh

LONG DURATION / NO TIME LIMIT
GLOBAL 'WAR ON TERROR' THEME

Hide & Seek

ROUND TWO

Obama Hides & Al-Qaeda
Have to Find Him

Countdown from Ten Organised by Tissot
Blindfolds by Tommy Hilfiger

—

Western Racists, 'Democrats', Morons & etc.
TAKE TO THE INTERNET
IN A HASTY DISPLAY OF PROUD IGNORANCE
BIN / 'BINNED' LADEN PUNS & SAND-MONKEY JOKES

Undereducated Caucasians & Uneducated Christians Welcome
Bring a Bottle & a Copy of The Old Testament

—

In the Car Park
'FAMILY OPEN DAY'

Members of the MET.
DEMONSTRATE THE USE OF
'Excessive & Unreasonable Force'

Last Man Standing. Winner Takes All.

GRUESOME PHOTOSHOP CONTEST

BIN LADEN'S CORPSE

Win a Semi-Legal Copy of Adobe Creative Suite or Similar

100 Runner Up Prizes Inc. Copies of iPhoto (Not Sympathetic to Windows)

—

Special Al-Qaeda Prize

Photoshop Bin Laden

So He Looks Like He is Not Really Dead

also

Photoshop Bin Laden

So He Looks Like He is Not Really Bin Laden

Special ISI Prize for Realistic Eyes. Special Navy Seals Prize for Reflections in Glistening Blood. Special Prize for Pathos. Plus Other Prizes t.b.c.

Also:

Diana Princess of Wales Gruesome Car Crash Photoshop Contest
Random Head Injury Photoshop Contest
Exploding Helicopter Photoshop Contest
Hindenberg Colourisation Photoshop Contest
Rotted Corpse Photoshop Contest
Eyes Rolling Out Photoshop Contest
Myra Hindley (sic) Photoshop Contest
Stack of Corpses Photoshop Contest
Random Drone Victims Photoshop Contest & Co.

The Very Best of

KATE MIDDLETON RAPE FANTASY FICTION

Volume #1

Sponsored by Hello Magazine & The Daily Mail

PLUS

First Past The Post

An Important Referendum About Nick Clegg

Results Announced by a Hypocrite. Judges' Decision is Final.

Gang Related Symphony Orchestra

Gang Related Gardening

PLUS

"The Life & Recent Death of Henry Cooper"
New Ballet Danced by Rudolph Nureyev (Deceased)
Inc. Dance of Pulverised Jawbones etc.
Music by Olivia Newton-John

—

Art in the Foyer

Amateur Photographs of Sellafield

The best new images from Daytrippers, Idiots,
Holiday Snappers, Architecture Students
& Other Al-Qaeda Reconnaissance Units

Installation of Cameras Everywhere

—

Dirge & Death March by an Orchestra of Complex Financial Instruments

(Charity Event)

—

Lie Detector Tests
for All Middle Management

—

The 'Ryan Air (sic) Effect'
All Night Drunken Braying of Touristic Scum

(Check Press for New Destinations)

plus

Mass Exodus of Economic Migrants

Talented Mimes Demonstrate

The 1000 Sad Faces
of Nick Clegg

(plus Support: 100 Supercilious Expressions of David Cameron)

—

French Football Contest

Majority White Teams Only

Strictly Apartheid 4-4-2 Formation

Blacks & Arabs only 30% Welcome

Goal Chances Pre-scheduled by New Racial Quota System

Plus: At Midnight

'Keeping the Game Clean' Gala Fundraiser for Segregated Shower Facilities

Tickets £300. Majority White Strippers. Majority White Waiters. Majority White Taxi Drivers. Majority White Everything etc.

—

Bin Laden's Funniest Home Videos

Inc. Hose Pipe Accident, Pakistan Pie-Face, Cat In A Mirror

& Hilarious "Al-Qaeda Style" Coca Cola & Mentos Prank

Plus – Two Men Shot Dead For No Apparent Reason

The Execution of a Teenage Dole Fraud Hung By The Neck from His Nylon Shell Suit Trousers. The Corpse Whipped Raw Using Headphones from His Sister's iPhone etc.

—

Lullabies in which the Lyrics Consist of Confusing Explanations
for Political Systems That Don't Exist Anywhere in the World

—

Nightmares About Escaping From Syria and Ending Up In Bahrain

—

City Farm Community Disco
Sponsored by Tesco
feat. Local Traders & Organic Dancefloor Lighting Rig

Christian Web Porn

Teenage SEXUAL Abstinence

Live on Camera 24:7

"What God's Right Hand is For"

—

GRAND SALE OF COOKERY BOOKS

Marco Pierre White – The Khmer Rouge Kitchen

Gordon Ramsay – Prison Food for Beginners

Jamie Oliver – Cooking with the Taliban (Inc. Goat & Chicken Surprise)

Delia Smith – Al-Qaeda Days, Guantanamo Nights (Inc. Pot Noodle, Cheese Sandwich & a Bottle of Fanta)

GRAND 'OPENING'

SOCIAL MOBILITY
"MUSEUM OF PARALYSIS"

Closed 24 Hours Daily. Monday–Sunday 9am–9am.
No Entrance for the Employed & Unemployed. No Entrance for Pensioners.
No Entrance for Students. No Concessions. No Wheelchair Access.

—

Modern Art Exhibition

Inc. Portraits of Life on a Traffic Island
in a Style Invented by Paul Gauguin

PLUS

'Performance Art'

Naked Girls Covered in Someone Else's Paint

PUERILE SENTIMENT

WATERBOARDING FOR FUN & PROFIT

Comedy Act Involving Rats

PLUS

Statue of a Man With His Head Blown Off
Statue of a Man With No Legs
Statue of a Woman that Has Been Blinded

Plus Other Statues t.b.c.

FANCY DRESS FIGHT

Men Dressed As Women

vs

Women Dressed as Alligators

Kids Dressed as Adults

vs

Adults Dressed as Teenagers

—

Soon-to-be-Supermodels

in

Disposable PRADA Underwear

—

Tsunami Nostalgia

Transgender Tupperware Party

POSTPONED

TWISTED IRANIAN PUNISHMENTS
TWO-FOR-ONE ALL WEEKEND

Tehran–Style Equivalent Justice

Let The Victims Choose / Let The Victims Pull The Lever /
Let The Victims Bite The Rapists' Balls Off etc.

—

Ludovico Treatment / All Nude Celebrity Screening

Cannes Special / Projectionist's Nightmare
All Films From The Festival Played Backwards,
Mixed Up & Out of Order
& Dialogue / Sound & Subtitles Out of Sync

All New Soundtracks by 200 DJs from Rotherham & The National Symphony Orchestra of Syria

PLUS

"Pirate Night"

Best Camcorder Movies of Movies
Inc. Toy Story 3D in 2D filmed past the Fat Head & Shoulders of some Bloke in the Next Row

Allegorical Drama / Ballet Mécanique

NO HOLDS
BARRED
NEW I.M.F. POLICY

Literal / Vigorous Enactment in New York Hotel

PLUS

SEX FANTASIES

OF THE WORLD'S MOST POWERFUL MEN

Special Guests: Dominique Strauss-Kahn & Nicolas Sarkozy

Next Week:
SEX FANTASIES OF WORLD'S POOREST MEN & Co.

—

EUROVISION SONG CONTEST
BACKWARDS / SATANIC RE-RUN

Guaranteed all songs played & sung BACKWARDS live without overdubs or your MONEY BACK
Backstage Security outsourced to Israeli Military. Votes Counted by David Willets.

THE EXTREME CUTTING EDGE
OF ESOTERIC ACOUSTICS & OCCULT POLITICS

N.H.S. LISTENING EXERCISE

DEAF MEN WITH OUIJA-DEVICES INTERVIEW BADLY SERVED PATIENTS FROM BEYOND THE GRAVE

"IN THE UNDERCLASS NO ONE CAN HEAR YOU SCREAM"

Real Life Quandaries of the Underclass #1 The Street Drinker's Dilemma

Inc. Sleep Rough or Blow Job
Share Needle or Go Without
Sleep in A Doorway or Keep Walking 'Til Morning
Starve or Shoplift
Soil Pants or Shit in the Bus Shelter

plus

Schrödinger's Cat

Spin the Strongbow Cider Bottle / Truth or Dare

—

In The Car Park
Andrew Lansley's Unnatural Consortia
plus Support t.b.c.

Conversational English for Call Girls, Rent Boys, Prostitutes & Escorts

Lesson One: Chit Chat

Inc.
"In My Country..."
"I like all kinds of music..."
"War is a terrible thing..."

Plus FREE Lesson Two: "Dirty Talk" & "Sexy Slang"

—

Gerry Adams & Martin McGuinness
Pay Their Respects at The Cenotaph
'A Wreath Woven of Shamrocks & Roses'

STUDENT THEATRE

presents

TWO MEN
HALF SLEEPING
HALF INTERNETTING

—

"Beautiful Speeches by a Lame Duck President"

—

'MEGA' DANCE BATTLE

**Partly-Roboticised White Kids
in Dirty Replica Designer Hoodies**

vs

**Entirely-Roboticised Asian Kids
in Spotless White Tracksuits**

Winner Stays On

Batteries Not Included

WORLD COMES TO AN END AT 6PM PROMPT

**No Latecomers
Ticketholders & Religious Nutcases Only**

PLUS

SUPERINJUNCTION SPECIAL

"Misuse of Modern (sic) Technology"

A FOOTBALLER WHOSE NAME CAN'T BE REVEALED HAS SEX WITH A CELEBRITY NO-ONE HAS HEARD OF
A SERIES OF UNFORTUNATE WOMEN HAVE SEX WITH JEREMY CLARKSON

& etc.

—

A SOLITARY ELEPHANT DROPPED WITHOUT PARACHUTE INTO THE RIVER FROM WESTMINSTER BRIDGE

RIVER THAMES SPLASH CONTEST

including:

Boris Johnson

dropped NAKED from a Helicopter

Sam Fox

dressed in a Trouser Suit & hurled from the Hungerford Bridge

Paul "Gazza" Gascoigne

bound in a REPLICA England KIT & launched from a Cannon at the Tower

Plus other guests t.b.c. Contains artificial LIGHTING.
Prizes at 10pm Prompt. No Crash Helmets, T-Shirts or Baseball caps.

—

Who Can Swim Like A Jellyfish?

Open to everyone. Win an iPad. British Citizens Only.

—

POST RAPTURE RETURN TO NORMALITY

Harold Camping Announces Revised Date For The End

On The Main Stage

RYAN GIGGS NOT DOING ANYTHING AT ALL

(Staged in Strict Accordance with the Law)

—

"ICELAND'S REVENGE"

INNOVATIVE NEW CHOREOGRAPHY OF VOLCANIC ASH

feat. Grímsvötn Volcano & Friends. Subsidised by the Air Travel Industry.

—

EROTIC EXTORTION
EXOTIC ABORTION
ABORTIVE EXODUS
AEROBIC DYSENTRY

—

MODERN DANCE

(FROM A NARROWLY DEFINED VERSION OF EUROPE)

Young Men Staring DEATH in the FACE

Talented Women DOING YOGA in FAECES

Music by a Famous Idiot. Lighting by Klaus Wunderlicht (sic).

THE SHIFTING PATTERNS
THE WIND MAKES
IN THE OTHERWISE STILLED WATER
OF A DIRTY RIVER AT NIGHT

—

IN THE FOYER
TOXIC FUMES

IN THE THEATRE
SUBSIDENCE

IN THE CAFÉ / BAR
ROAD-KILL CHIHUAHUA
& ANTEATER SANDWICHES

—

Best Drunken Japes of the Air Traffic Control Room at Heathrow
VS
Best Out-takes From Gatwick CCTV

Inc. Trolley Collision, 'Passive Smokers', Man Urinates in Prayer Room,
'Suitcase Full of Bondage Gear'

Two People That Cannot Be Named for Legal Reasons Holding An Object That Cannot Be Named For Legal Reasons Sitting in a Place that Cannot Be Named for Legal Reasons & Doing Something That Cannot Be Described for Legal Reasons

PLUS

Sans Titre "New Choreography"

Based Loosely on

The Downward Spiral of People's Lives

Any Resemblance to Actual Persons Living or Dead is Entirely Coincidental

Sex Fantasies of the Jihadists
Sex Fantasies of the Christian Right
Sex Fantasies of the Flat Earthers

OBAMA & CAMERON
"MODERN BRITAIN MEET THE YOUTH PING PONG TOUR"

**Inc. SINK SCHOOLS, DE-FUNDED YOUTH PROJECTS, CRACKHOUSES,
BLACK ON BLACK CRIME HOT-SPOTS
& SITES OF RACIST MURDERS**

**Plus Photo Op with Asstd. Low Ranking Royals, Corgis, Stonehenge,
Oxoford University (sic), The Mary Whitehouse Cliffs of Dover, Vera Lynn,
Jimmy Tarbuck, Baked Beans & Big Ben**

plus

LUNCHTIME ENTERTAINMENT
**LENNY HENRY TAP DANCES WITH
NICK CLEGG IN HIDEOUS MARMITE BLACKFACE**
&
**MICHELLE OBAMA & THE CAST OF EASTENDERS
SING COCKERNEY ANTHEMS OF THE 1980s**
Inc. GOTTA PICK A POCKET OR TWO,
"SOCIAL EQUALITY FOR LOSERS",
A STAR SPANGLED BANNER etc.

Longest Running International Hide & Seek

Ratko Mladic vs UN War Crimes Tribunal

New World Hiding Record. Winner Declared. Preliminary Interrogation of the Loser.

—

Alleged Rapists in Suits

Dominique Strauss-Kahn & Julian Assange

Deny All Allegations & Discuss Classic Men's Clothing & Accessories

PLUS

In the Basement

Unabomber Chic: Panel Discussion

Lone White Males, Serial Rapists & Child Abductors of the Modern Era

Discuss Sweat Pants & The 'Dos & Don'ts' of Sports Store & Supermarket Style

The Corpse of an ANIMAL Given Vague Animation & Appearance of LIFE Thanks to the Movement of SMALL FLIES Within

—

A Meeting with NO PURPOSE and NO FIXED DURATION
All welcome. No Latecomers. Now with AIR CONDITIONING.

—

Special Guess Appearance

Her Royal Highness the Duchess of CambReiss

Katreiss Middleton

Coin Throwing Contest

THROW A COIN IN DAVID CAMERON'S MOUTH

Win a Jail Sentence

(Does NOT Affect Your Statutory Rights)

No Entry for Old Etonians. No Foreign Coins. No Euros.

Extra Prizes for Knocking Out Teeth.

Sponsored by The British Dental Association in Conjunction with Polyfilla

Terms & Conditions May Apply. Contents May Settle During Shipping.

Entries May Be Recorded For Military Training Purposes

Judged by Cheryl Cole's Hairdresser's Sister's Boyfriend's Uncle or Brother-in-Law

FIFA AUCTION

World Cup Locations To Highest Bidder

CASH ONLY

Plus

In the Newly Fortified Basement
Offside Corruption Karaoke
"Soccer Accusations Sing-A-Long Style"

feat. Reynald Temarii, Amos Adamu, Roger Burden, Jack Warner,
Sepp Blatter, Chuck Blazer and Mohamed Bin Hammam & Co.

—

David Cameron's Golden Bathroom Guided Tour

Music by Andrew Lloyd Webber. Free Golden Shower for the first FIVE unmarried MOTHERS.

FIGHT MARATHON

People Who Are So Tired & Empty & Exhausted They Can't Even Cry

VS

People Who Are So Numb, Beaten, Vacant & Internally Petrified That They Can't Even Move

—

People Who Are Ashamed of Their Ancestors

VS

People Who Are Ashamed of Themselves

—

Men With Blood On Their Hands

VS

Women With Hands Down Their Trousers

Judged by Ryan Giggs & Cheryl Cole PLUS Imogen Thomas t.b.c.

Win an iPad plus Runner Up Prizes Inc. Box of Generic Groceries by Lidl

& a Bouquet of Mutated Dandelions From Sellafield

—

Late-Capitalist Lullabies

AT ABSOLUTELY DEAFENING VOLUME

URBAN TRANSFORMATION DAY

**Schoolchildren
Transform a Dingy Subway
into A Futuristic Prison**

**Street Drinkers
Transform a Children's Playground
into a Vast Experimental Urinal**

**Property Developers
Turn a Mixed Race Housing Estate
into a Whites Only Fortress
for Wealthy Bachelor Idiots**

—

CLINGING TO POWER

Masterclass by Silvio Berlusconi, Sepp Blatter & Muammar Gaddafi

Three Tenacious Old Lunatics
Show You Exactly How to Keep Hold of the Reins

NEXT WEEK: STEVE JOBS & BILL GATES

Any Willing Sadists & 'Care Quality Commission' (sic)

presents

Vulnerable Adults Olympics

Inc. Autistic Teenager Baiting, Retardo-Pinching, Spaz-Slapping

'New Modes of Restraint' Contest

Patients Trapped Under & Inside Furniture & etc.
Big Cash Prizes. Big Share Dividends.

Next Week:

MASTERCLASS

Granny Farming for the Greedy & Immoral

"Turn Other People's Toothless Bedwetting, Senility & Misfortune into Your Retirement Nest Egg"

All Profit, All of the Time.

CONSTANT SOUNDTRACK OF DAYTIME TELEVISION

in the 'garden'

BARELY LIVING SCULPTURE

"80 CANTANKEROUS CANCEROUS INCONTINENT BIG MOUTH WAR VETERANS TIED TO A CHAIR"

—

The Latest in Deregulation & Privatisation Patient-Care Equipment

'Black Hole of Calcutta' / PENSIONER PUNISHMENT BLOCK
Flat Pack Solitary & Self-Assembly Holding-Tank Facility

A MUST FOR ALL CARE HOMES. Capacity 50-100 approx. Govt Approved. Coin Operated.

SQUALID DAYDREAMS

—

THE WORST PAIN ON EARTH

—

A MILLION POUNDS WORTH OF FIREWORKS SPELLING OUT WORDS THAT NO ONE CAN READ

EUROPEAN TOUR
E. Coli 0104:H4

plus support

Inc. Germany, Austria, Denmark, Holland, Norway, Spain, Sweden, Switzerland, UK, Czech Republic, France and the USA.

Further Dates t.b.c. Not suitable for People.

—

Staring Contest

Men With No Time
vs
Women With No Hope

Hypnotised Kids
vs
Tranquilised Hypnotists

Ali Abdullah Saleh
vs
Hamid al-Ahmar

Judged by Simon Cowell's Botox Doctor & Jack 'Dr. Death' Kevorkian (Deceased)

Win a Parking Ticket to Olympics. One Entry Per Family.

June 5 2011

COLLECTED SEPTIC PIGEON SHIT OF THE VENICE BIENNALE

"Hand–Harvested Turds of Exquisite Execrement (sic)"

Post–Soviet / New Money Drinks Reception
Curated by Dasha Zhukova

feat. Tasteful Avant-Garde Toilet, Solid Gold Pubic Centrepiece & Innovative Seating Plan
VIP Coke & Cocktails. 10,000 Exclusive Guests That Have Been Surgically Plasticised.

—

Late Night Talk Event
"What's In A Name?"

Roman Signer & Roman Abramovich in conversation with Marina Warner & Marina Abramovic

Memories of the Royal Wedding

**A Sensitive Tribute by People Who Actually Think They Were There
With Music by Lemon Gusset & Aspartame Prokofiev (sic)**

Half-Time Infommercial by Werner Herzog. Lighting by Albert Speer.
Free Servants, Tea & Scones.

—

Wayne Rooney
"Total Head Transplant"

PLUS OTHER TRANSPLANTS t.b.c.

—

Muhammad Ilyas Kashmiri Dead Again

Old Men & Old Women REMEMBER '**WHAT THINGS USED TO BE LIKE**' Young People try their BEST to FORGET

plus

Experimental Crowd Control from Syria

—

In the Basement

One Hit Wonders

"Sleazy Migraine Music"

PLUS SUPPORT by BONO'S TAX ADVISOR
Free Salad of Spanish Cucumber & German Beansprouts for Everyone
(plus other ingredients t.b.c.)

New Public Holidays
CELEBRATING

Historic Defeats, Disasters, Massacres, Economic Collapses & Failed Revolutions

—

Kids from the suburbs are blinded by Gerard Depardieu wearing a Rustical Period Costume envisaged by Laura Ashley

Kids in the Hijab do mental gymnastics on the topic of freedom

Kids from Fame (on VHS video)

—

CRISIS TALKS
OF THE SYRIAN TOURIST BOARD
SET TO BORING MUSIC BY COLDPLAY

**DRAMATISED VOICEMAIL MESSAGES OF KATE MIDDLETON
AS BROUGHT TO LIFE BY A CAST OF 200 SEMI-FAMOUS ACTORS
DIRECTED BY SIR PETER HALL & SIR PETER BROOK
MUSICAL ACCOMPANIEMENT BY SIR PETER MAXWELL DAVIES
DREAM SEQUENCES CHOREOGRAPHED BY A MAN THAT ONCE KNEW
A MAN THAT KNEW A MAN THAT KNEW SIGMUND FREUD (DECEASED)**

—

Political Stand-Up Comedy from Washington

Anthony Weiner

"Weiner Jokes Marathon"

**Inc. 'HIDE THE WEINER' 'BATTLE OF THE BULGE',
'MY WEINER IS SHRINKING' & 'SUCK ON IT BITCH' etc.**

Plus Support
Making His Political Comeback (sic)
Bill 'Blow Me' Clinton

Beauty Contests

Miss Euro Bailout
Miss Economic Isolation
Miss Solitary Confinement
Miss Money Laundering
Miss Separation and Depression
Miss Privatisation
Miss Exploitation
Miss Anti-Matter
Miss Matter
Miss Manners
Miss Acceptable Racism
Miss Syria
Miss Prescription Tranquilisers
Miss Phone Hacking
Miss Slow Death
Miss Democracy
Miss Exit
Miss Goodbye

Non-Consensual Pixelised Childhood

Auto-Erotic Auto-Focus 38 Inch Mega-Penis. Fully Manual. Zeiss Zoom to Wide-Open Legs feat. Super Night Shot Facility

—

"Sarah Palin's Emails"
(December 2006 to September 2008)
Set to Supposedly New Music by Ancient Athabascan & Inuit fiddlers
Barbeque of Seafood in a Sauce of Oil & Natural Gas

plus

Cabaret 'Homage to Gaga'
Eskimo Strippers in Whale Meat Corsets
Inc. Legal Affidavit Served by Jana Sterbak

In the Cafeteria
"Repression à la Carte"
"Melancholia à la Mode"

All Dishes Served Cold

STRAY DOGS are SET ON FIRE
then LAUNCHED INTO SPACE
By uniformed members of the French Foreign Legion

Teenagers Laugh at EACH OTHER OLD MEN laugh at Cameron, MERKEL & SARKOZY

On the Main Stage

Public Confessions by
Corrupt Officials in the Housing Department, City Traders & Numerous Eurocrats

Outside

Parisian Housewives on a non-lethal Cocktail of Alcohol & prescription tranquilisers
Dance to some Music which no one else can HEAR

June 13 2011

THE
FUNFAIR
AT
JISR
AL-SHUGHOUR

ALL RIDES HALF PRICE

HALL OF BLOOD & MIRRORS

"ROCK, SHOCK & ROLLER COASTER"

BURNING FARMLAND / AMATEUR BREAST REDUCTION

PRIZES PRESENTED BY A DWARF

ABSOLUTELY NO REFUNDS

ELECTRICAL IMPULSES IN THE BRAIN OF AN ALSO RAN

—

"THE BIG HISS" SILENCES SAMPLED FROM MOVIES EDITED TOGETHER TO MAKE A LONGER SILENCE

—

'Innoviative (sic) Theatre'

Coalition 'Debates' on the N.H.S.

Re-Enacted using Puppets made from Morgue Residue & Hazardous Hospital Waste
Voices by Keir Hardie & David Cronenburger
Background Music by Chas, Dave & The Anaesthetists Skiffle Band
Heartrending strings by the London Sympathy Orchestra

Exhibition of Bad Atmospheres

Inc.

Kebab House Saturday
Ryanair 6am Staffroom
Nick Clegg Bedroom Anytime

PLUS

All New Perfume Promotion

feat.

Le Spirit de Divorce
Spunktacular by Givenchy
Eau de Life Sentence

& other smells t.b.c.

—

Fukishima (sic) Meltdown: New Single: Triple A Side
Mutant Fingers / TEPCO Half-Life / Forgotten But By No Means Gone

All Nude Euro MPs "Ritual Dance Against Debt Contagion"

—

People Who Are So Lonely That They Explode or Shatter When Touched

—

Trial by Tabloid
Trial by Error
Trial by Negligent Council
Trial by Man in Négligée
Trial by Calculator
Trial by Brain Death
Trial by Weighbridge
Trial by Neighbourhood Watch
Trial by Mob
Trial by Racists
Trial by Youths
Trial by Cops
Trial by Torchlight
Trial by Electricity

PLUS OTHER TRIALS t.b.c.

Men That Can't Take It Any More

vs

Women That Can't Take Anything Seriously

—

LECTURE DEMONSTRATION

Weiner
Withdrawal
Method

(INTERNET READY. PLUG IN AND PLAY).

—

Economic E. Coli / Greek Diarrhoea
Served with a Side Dish of Tear Gas
& Kolokithia Yemista

Temporary Chef: George Papandreou
Restaurant Music by George Michael (New Album "Let them eat Cobblestones...")

The Suburbs & The Centre Trade Places for a Day

RAP MUSIC & BREAKDANCE CONTEST
in the CARPARK of a SUPERMARKET
All Welcome. Not sponsored by Nike.

Men and women make long boring declarations of LOVE
French language is defended against IMPROPER INFUENCES

In the PRIVATE GARDEN

Charlotte Gainsbourg
gives a realistic MIME of a SEXUAL ACTION

(Free Internet & 500 text messages)

June 19 2011

Quick, Cheap & Painless
Death for Unwanted Animals

All DAY PET DESTRUCTION AMNESTY

Rabbits Dispatched to a Better Place

Dogs & Cats Drowned

**Gerbils Executed
in a
Paddling Pool of Tears**

Arsenic, Cyanide & Shit-flavoured Homogenised Niche-Packaged Smug, Bland, Self-Satisfied SHRINK WRAPPED TRANS-NATIONAL & Entirely Apolitical

YOUTH CULTURE

One Fits All. Available in WHITE only*.
(*with Hint of Afro, Asia or Latina Beat)

As seen in Prinz Lauberg (sic), Bushwick, Shoreditch etc.
Free Hipster Jeans & a Stupid Fucking T-Shirt for Anyone

—

IN THE BEER GARDEN
"Involuntary Euthanasia"

While Rome (or Equivalent) Burns

Pres. Assad Explains Structure of a Committee to Discuss Formation of Committees to Discuss Agenda for Possible Future Committees & etc.

No Fiddlers. No Microbes. No Germs. No Agitators.

PLUS

Euro Exchange Rate
Rapid-Chargrilled on a Bed of Athens

A Long Boring Day in the Life of Mikhail Khodorkovsky

High Security Door Entry System
"Asshole Recognition Software"

feat. Hygienic Probe for Rectal Insertion, Reclaimed Wet Wipes & etc.

Procedure carried out by a Semi-Qualified Nurse who looks a bit like Warren Beatty

The Massively Amplified Sound of a Hard Drive Fan Struggling Because the Laptop has been Placed 'Carelessly' Under a Duvet

—

Street Drinkers Olympics
Crack Olympics
Farting Olympics

—

Imaginary Brain Surgery

—

FIGHT NIGHT

Internet Lepers

vs

People With 10,000 Facebook Friends

Win a Vestibule or other French Stuff

DICTATOR MENTORING
WHAT TO DO NEXT?

Hamad bin Isa al-Khalifa KING of Bahrain
& President Bashar al-Assad of Syria
DISCUSS TACTICS WITH
Hosni Mubarak (formerly Egypt)
& Ben Ali (formerly Tunisia)

Plus SPECIAL GUEST Nicolae Ceausescu (Deceased) (Formerly Romania) (Skype Appearance)
No Translation. No Seats – Everyone Sits on the Floor or Stands Against the Wall. No Protests. No Questions.

—

Post Wedding / Post Honeymoon / Post Photoshoot

Guess the Weight of the Princess

Closest Guess Wins A Night at Her Majesty's Pleasure

—

In the Basement

International Cabaret of BotNets

"Smug Pig Expressions of David Cameron"

Emotional Parilysis (sic)

No Support

June 24 2011

Good News Chorus

Celebrities Covered in Syrup
Read Rhyming Headlines
of Hope & Celebration
From Unfortunate Parts of the Globe

Music Composed by Beyoncé's Backing Singer's Brother
Also feat. Waterproof White Costumes,
Stuffed Doves Crucified in the Shape of a Sponsor's Logo etc.

3% of Proceeds to Charity

—

"BEST" OF TV #35

**Dead Cameraman
Epileptic Interview
Incontinent Sports Commentator
Vomiting Weatherman
Talk Show Mass Sphincter Fail**

plus

From The Archive

THE ALL TIME USER-VOTED HILARIOUS CLASSIC

"Schizophrenic Newsreader"
(Voices in Ear vs Voices in Head)

A General Non-Treatable Tendency to Despair

PLUS

Experimental Botox
Men with Formaldehyde Faces
Women With Polyfilla Smiles

Win a Free Medical Consultation with an Idiot

—

Eye for an Eye / Pixel for a Pixel

Biblical Justice for Internet Criminals

Illegal Downloaders Have Sections of Brain Downloaded

Identity Fraudsters Copied, Cloned & Abused at Long Distance

Spammers Taken to Restaurant
& Subjected To Denial of Service Attack

Hacker Groups PHP Scripting Contest: Win A Job at Oracle

—

The Amazing Selective Memory of John Galliano

Peter Falk Investigates
(Final Episode)

Life After Death

Next Week:

Case Closed / Cold Case / Eternity

Hacking It Up At The Hague / Going Dutch

Celebration of Cultural Dismemberment

feat.
Symphony of Cuts

Composed & Conducted in INCOMPETENT HASTE by Halbe Zijlstra
"Cultural Policy as an Instrument of National Division & Shame"

Partially Amplified Poverty

Fingers in Dykes & Clogs
Sensible Protestant Art-Haters

Old Masters Forever / New Art to the Wall

—

Senior Conservatives:
Bus Trip To Glastonbury
ALL WELCOME

**A Tawdry Miasma of Superficial Sense
Skimmed Across a Toxic**

Bottomless
Ocean of Bile

—

Van Gogh's Ear Museum

Closed Due to Further Cutbacks

Late Night Cinema
"Foreign Nonsense"

**Slow Films Without Car Chases
Long Tracking Shots
Half Naked Girls With Subtitles & Unusual Accents**

plus

Cell Animation of the Former Russian Gulags

Diagram of a Room That Has No Exits*

(*probably not produced using AutoCAD)

—

Best of Internet Animal Immolation #6

Cat Fire
Dog Fire
Wolves in Petrol
Parrot in Lighter Fluid
Burning Swans
Sheep in Flames
Slug in a Toaster

—

INTERNATIONAL PISSING CONTEST

North Korea vs South Korea

feat. Kim Jong-il & Lee Myung-bak. Win a Peninsula.

In The Basement / Rare Public Appearance

"GOD CLARIFIES THE NATURE & LEVEL
OF HIS SUPPORT FOR MICHELE BACHMANN"

June 30 2011

George Papandreou
& His Syntagma Square Orchestra

The Sound of People Gagging & Retching From Teargas Simulated on an Organ & Played in an Up-tempo Greek Bossa Nova Style

feat. 2 Singers With Big Asses & 58 Wounded Backing Dancers

—

Historical Arm Wrestling – The Despots / Mixed Doubles

Genghis Khan & Margaret Thatcher

vs

Adolf Hitler & Cleopatra

A Musical Tribute to Loneliness
feat. Songs That Try to Put a Positive Spin on It

Live Performances by
Adele or Katy Perry (t.b.c.)
Dolly Parton (Deceased)
Elvis Presley Museum
Frank Sinatra (Deceased)

'House Band'
Forever Electrocution

—

Unwanted Shadows of The Past Loom Large & Unnaturally Vivid in a Present which Everyone Prefers to Forget

—

"POST STRIKE GENERAL CHAOS & Industrial Inaction"

A Story About Giants Enacted by Dwarves

Simultaneous Blow Jobs & DOUBLE JOINTED Ambidextrous Hand Jobs Marathon

Free Hotdogs & A Warm Drink For All Contestants

—

In The Basement

Partially Exclusive Stage-Show
Jamie Hince & Kate Moss in 'Concert'

Farrah Fawcett–Majors in A Red Swimsuit

**The breath KNOCKED OUT
of an Old Age Pensioner**

Financial Markets 'Slump, Dump, Bump & Grind Night'

Free Entry for Rich People

NO HOODIES
NO TRAINERS
NO BASEBALL CAPS

—

"THE TALK OF THE TOWN"

Top Down Democracy Disco

Three Illuminated Dancefloors. Two Bars. One Person One Vote.

—

Dictatorship of the Idiot-ariat

Mug of Tea for Everyone
Light Bondage & Lightweight Chitter Chatter

American Amnesia
American Barbarism
American Botox
American Cabaret
American Comedy
American Death
American Embassies
American Erotica
American Esoterica
American Espionage
American Flag
American Ghosts
American Guns
American Healthcare
American Homeless
American Ideologues
American Lies
American Mall
American Money
American Nepotism
American Nukes
American Pie
American Porn
American Prison
American Rape
American Silicon
American Slavery
American Trash
American Torture
American Walmart
American War
American Wishes
American Xenophobia

'Live' on Stage

EROTICA OF THE VANITIES

MEN

Surrounded By Bodyguards

Make Love to

WOMEN

Surrounded by Personal Assistants

—

Papier-mâché Effigies of the Underclass
Left Out to Go Sodden in the Rain

—

Semi-Musical Typewriters
Compose a Symphony of Letters to the D.H.S.S.
Win A Prize But Lose Your Benefits

HETEROSEXUAL SHIPWRECKED SAILORS

THAT DO NOT TAKE IT UP THE ASS

NEW COMMUNITANICAL OPERA WITH SCRIPT BY LEE HALL HAND CENSORED BY A MOB OF LOVING PARENTS

Production Artistically Mediated Out of Existence by Opera North & East Riding Council

GUARANTEED NO GAY CHARACTERS OR YOUR MONEY BACK

PLUS

PRO-STYLE TRAINING SEMINAR
"The Lower Depths of Journalism"
News International

PHONE HACKING A HIGHER ASTRAL PLANE

Next Week: Celebrity Foetal Voicemail

—

Ballet Reconstructive
The Last Tangled Pencil Marks of Cy Twombly
Music: The Tracks of My Tears

ON THE MAIN STAGE

"ALL IN A GOOD CAUSE" Ballet Troupe of Dead Soldiers

PERFORM A POWERFUL CELEBRATION OF WAR THROUGH THE AGES

PLUS

ON THE BORIS JOHNSON 'LONDON BOMBINGS MEMORIAL STAGE'

Shoreditch Klansmen
Fiscal Lunatics
Khmer Rouge of Rap
DJ Dambuster
DJ Just Dammer
DJ Jackhammer

Also feat. Cops with Inflatable Self-Lubricating Truncheons
Al-Qaeda Theme Foam Party / Space Cakes
The Greatest Taser Show on Earth (15,000 Megavolts)
A Swimming Pool Filled with Cocaine

—

A Story About Wisdom Enacted by Fools

News Internationalist
Kamikaze Journalism Training Course

Part One

Advanced Ethics Mangling
& Total Disregard of Law

Inc.
Listening into a Telephone
Bribing an Officer / Hiding in the Corner of an Office
Impersonating Grief Counsellors
Dressing Up as a Priest (Bring Own Costume)
Interview by Hypnotism / Negative Truth Serum
Cartoon of a Suicide Covered in a Union Jack
A Pig in Wolf's Clothing ('All' Proceeds to Charity)

PLUS

"Going Undercover Amongst Human Beings"

Next Week
Course Cancelled Due to Faux Contrition & Total Lack of Newspaper

—

A Story about Virgins Enacted by Whores

Anti Nuclear Flamenco

Free Market Samba Class

Tickets €50. Compulsory Cloakroom & Valet Parking €500.

—

Strictly Boardroom

Tango with Rupert / Foxtrot with James
Dance Class for Party Leaders

Sponsored by Rupert 'The Vote Catcher' Murdoch
Compère Rebekah Brooks (Topless)
Judged by the Press Complaints Commission (Gutless)
Win a Car, a Microwave & 3 Litres of Unleaded Petrol

—

A Story About Good Men Enacted by Incompetent Thieves

July 10 2011

DADA POETRY NIGHT

NOW
NOW NO MORE NEWS OF THE WORLD
NO MORE NEWS OF
NEWS OF THE WORLD
NOW
NO MORE NEWS OR WORLD
NO MORE WORLD
NO MORE WORLD OF NEWS
NOW
NO MORE NEWS
NOW
NO
MORE
WORLD NOW
NO MORE NOW

Starts at Dawn

Sony / Schweppes & Unilever 'Cabaret Voltaire Memorial Stage'

Performed by Andy Coulson & Tristan Tzara (Deceased)

Free Entry for Wapping Workers / Ex-Workers
All Proceeds to Saving Murdoch's Bid For BSkyB

On the AOLTimeWarner 'Berlin Dada Stage'

Great Shakespearean Actors
Read Half-a-Terabyte of Deleted Emails
from News International

Inc. Dame Peggy Ashcroft (Deceased) as King Lear, Ralph Fiennes as Hamlet,
Sarah Bernhardt (Deceased) as Orphemia (sic)
& Edmund Kean (Deceased) as Troilus and Cressida

Special Guest Appearance by Kenneth Branagh as The Fool

—

An Orchestra
of Beautiful Women That Fart
Play a Selection of Great Tunes
from The Hit Parade

Inc. Coldpay (sic) Every Teardrop is a Waterfall & Snoop Dog Sweat.
Tickets 50 Guineas. Free Champagne & Bouquet Garni for Everyone.

BLIND MEN IN BLING

—

FLASH PHOTOS OF A MORON REFLECTED IN A MIRROR

—

Michele Bachmann
Gets ALL NOSTALGIAC (sic) & FAMILY VALUES LIKE
ON THE TOPIC OF SLAVERY

JEREMY HUNT
RUPERT MURDOCH

&

PLACEBO DOMINGO (sic)
SING A LOVE DUET

TO

REBEKAH BROOKS

NOT REALLY SUITABLE FOR CHILDREN OR ANIMALS
WITH MUSIC ACCOMPANIEMENT (sic) FROM A CHORUS OF THE PHONE-HACKED

—

A Story About Virtue Enacted by Sluts

Telltale Nosebleeds
of the Rich & Famous

Partly Illustrated Lecture

—

Exhibition of Forged Paintings

Sunflowers by Van Gogh by Otto Wacker,
Water Lilies by Claude Monet by Anonymous (Not Internet Group)
& Realistic Rembrandt Landscape of a Multi-Storey Car Park at Dusk by Tom Keating
Plus other forgeries t.b.c.

—

The Fluctuating Share Price
of News International
Depicted in a Wild Dance
by Sultry and / or Toothless
"Romanian Roma Girls"

Music by Dole Scrounger Violinists, Fiddlers & Vocalists,
"the girls getting lower & lower to the ground
as the share price plummets, the gypos applauding"
Sponsored by Express Newspapers

TOP TEN
Racist RANTS
of the Internet
Delivered in the ALLCAPS Style

—

Great Car Crashes from History
(Simultaneous Stereoscopic Reconstruction)

Inc. James Dean, General George S. Patton, Lisa Lopes, Princess Grace, Albert Camus, Princess Diana, Jackson Pollock, Roland Barthes, Jayne Mansfield & Isadora Duncan.

Music by Peter Gabriel's Chyroproactor (sic)
Sponsored by Toyota

—

"How to Evacuate the Planet"
Experts help Prepare Citizens for the Pretty Much Inevitable

Inc. How to Build a Rocket, How to Dig a Grave, Symptoms of Bird Flu etc.

—

**The Chirpy Red Cheeked Bullshit of David Cameron
Showered with Molten Disdain**

SUNDRY CIRCUSES

Circus of Mice
Circus of Lab Rats
Circus of Death
Circus of Former Investment Bankers
Circus of Blood
Circus of Snipers
Circus of Elephants
Circus of Knots
Circus of Money
Circus of Shame
Circus of Circles
Circus of Rape
Circus of Nations
Circus of Fate
Circus of Knives
Circus of Frogs
Circus of Small Things
Circus of Silver
Circus of Gold
Circus of Cholera
Circus of Ambivalence
Circus of Subterfuge
Circus of AIDS
Circus of Chemistry
Circus of Mixed Feelings
Circus of Timewasting
Circus of Ballot Rigging

Plus FREE BREAD
& Other Circuses t.b.c.

SUMMER SPECIAL
TOXIC TOURISM

"THE BRITS ARE COMING"

Adulterated Beer Drinking Contest
FOLLOWED BY
Balconeering / Bareback Car Surfing

High Diving From The Mezzanine
Swimming Pool Filled With Lager, Vomit, Sunblock, Spermicide & Ouzo

LATE NIGHT SPECIAL
Locals vs Visitors
Fist Fights / Knife Fights

Pants on Head / Arse Out of Window
Offensive Behaviour Contest
Win A Vodka Enema

—

PRISONER CELL BLOCK F
Charlie Gilmour in Animated Leg Irons

Lyrics by Roger Waters. Music by David Gilmour.
Vocals by Syd Barrett. Original Artwork of the Cenotaph by Gerald Scarfe.

Everything Must Go

Corrupt & / Or Compromised High Ranking Police Officers,
Tabloid Editors, News Executives & Politicians

Three-For-One
Public Resignation Special
ALL WELCOME

**ALL Positions MUST be EMPTY by End of Week
GO NOW & GET A FREE BAG TO PUT THE STUFF FROM YOUR DESK IN
PLUS RESIGNATION SPEECHES DRAFTED HALF-PRICE
SIGNED PHOTO OF SILVIO BERLUSCONI & SOUVENIR MOUSE-MAT**

—

IN THE BASEMENT

LIVE SEX SHOW

DAVID CAMERON & RUPERT MURDOCH
"THE KAMA SUTRA OF THE FREE PRESS"

Special Guest Appearances: Rebekah 'Bukkake' Brooks,
Andy '9 inches' Coulson & Sir Paul Stephenson

Eurozone Philosophers TRAPPED in

Mental Quicksand

Gagging Orders of the Gutter Press

Artificial Insinuation / Artificial Insemination

The Olympics of Boasting
The Olympics of Bigotry
The Olympics of Numbness
The Olympics of Torture
& other Olympics t.b.c.

Rent Troubles: A Musical Burlesque

Lyrics by an IDIOT. Music by a FOOL.
Free ADMISSION for PROLETARIANS

NEPOTISTIC CABARET

—

JOURNALISTS POSING AS BEGGARS
INTERVIEW PHILOSOPHERS
DRESSED UP AS TOADS

—

CONTRITION COACHED & ELDERLY
"MAGNATES IN FOAM"
LIVE IBIZA STYLE PARLIAMENTARY QUESTIONS & BUCK-PASSING PARTY

—

PLUS

SLUMP IDOL
AMERICAN MARKET CRASH

GLAD RAGS TO NEGATIVE RICHES
JUDGED BY JACK LEW, JIM JORDEN & JOHN KYL

THEME TUNE BY NICOLE PRESCOVIA ELIKOLANI VALIENTE SCHERZINGER
& CHERYL COLE (NÉE TWEEDY)

Shopping Channel Live Special

All New Products of the Al-Qaeda Weapons Workshop

Belly Bomb / Mouth Bomb
Ass Bomb
Cunt Bomb
Ear, Nose & Throat Bomb

FREE SAMPLES / PRODUCT TESTING

—

LIARS PRETENDING TO BE MORALISTS SCRUTINISE TRAITORS CAMOUFLAGED AS FOOLS

The Strange Feeling of Sudden Descent that People sometimes Experience in Dreams

Free Cocktail of Saline & insulin for Latecomers

"Help Keep Waiting Lists Down"

BBC Sound Effects Library Vol. 4352

COLLECTED SOUNDS OF ECONOMIC DEPRESSION

Based on field recordings from all over Europe
Inc. Zero Investment (2 seconds), Nervous Markets (9 seconds),
Low Interest Rates (5 years)

plus

Barack Obama Trapped Hard Against A Debt Ceiling

—

Socialist Summer Camp

Experimental Arts, Politics, Youth & Community Programme

Ballet of the Island Utøya

Choreographed by Anders Behring Breivik

Lucifer Music Prize Awarded by Karlheinz Stockhausen (Deceased)

Sponsored by the Norwegian Tourist Board

RATS DESERT A SINKING SHIP
feat. NEW MUZACK BY JAMES MURDOCH'S DENTAL HYGENIST

PLUS

The Decline & Fall of Westernised Culture as Filmed from the Windows of a Speeding 4X4

Additional Interview Material by John Pilger
Music by a Girl That Looks Like Mariah Carey & a Guy Who Smells Like Engelbert Humperdink (Deceased)

—

In the "Carlsberg / Sapporo / Murphy's © Beer Garden"

A Story about Visions written in Braille

In The Newly Opened Upstairs O2 Vodaphone Arena

AMY WINEHOUSE (DECEASED) REUNION CONCERT

Lighting by Thomas Edison
Dances by Salome

—

In the Putrefied Sub-Basement

100–Strong Chorus of Mock-Repentant
TABLOID HACKS & PAPARAZZI
Sing LAMENTS & DIRGES
In TRADITIONAL FLEET STREET STYLE

Crocodile Tears Compulsory
Bring Your Own Whiskey. Bring Your Own Cocaine.
Flash Photography Not Permitted

NIHILISTIC BREAKFAST BUFFET

NON-EXAGGERATED HYPERBOLE

ORIGAMI VORTICES

—

At Midnight on the Harry Secombe Lower Stage
"The Goode Olde Camden–Flat Doorstepping Days"
Hacks & Paps Trade Tall Stories & Self-Aggrandising Platitudes of Amy & Blake

MODERN HORSE SHIT

FEAT. BOTTOM-UP / FACE-DOWN INTERACTIVE TENDENCIES

WEB 2.0 'WIKI DEATH CAMP' WORKSHOP

CROWD SOURCING GENOCIDE

HELP IMPROVE THE SPEED & EFFICIENCY OF YOUR OWN INDUSTRIALISED MURDER

ALMOST ALL WELCOME

**PRIZES PRESENTED BY PRINCE CHARLES,
MARK ZUCKURBERG (sic),
A FORMER MISS WORLD & A PREVIOUS RUNNER–UP
IN THE "PRIX DE MAO" USER–GENERATED AGRICULTURE CONTEST**

—

THE FACES OF THE MISSING

&

THE ECHOES OF THE DEAD

WEAK GROWTH
FEEBLE GROWTH
LOW GROWTH
NO GROWTH

—

BREAKFAST WITH NEWS CORE
LUNCH WITH NEWS CORE
DINNER WITH NEWS CORE
BED WITH NEWS CORE
WAKING UP WITH NEWS CORE

—

In The Annex

WAR BETWEEN THE ANIMALS

**A MAN IN A BEAR COSTUME
FIGHTS TWO CHILDREN
DRESSED AS AN OCTOPUS**

Re-Branded Greek Tourist Board

ATTRACTIONS OF THE MONTH

Parthenon / Acropolis of Debt
The Temple of Economic Contagion (formerly Temple of Poseidon)
Merkel Hill (formerly Lycabettus Hill)
Sarkozy Square (formerly Syntagma Square)

PLUS BEGGARS & SOARING CRIME RATES
MINOR MONUMENTS & STATUES WITH SOME BITS MISSING

In the Car Park

Premature Ejaculation
Premature Balding
Premature Burial
Pre-Senile Dementia
Pre-Historic Animals

—

JELLO WRESTLING

Men in Space Suits

vs

Women in Haute Couture

Winner Stays In. All Contestants Win a Bottle of Diet Coke.

Duel in the Sand

GOOD ARABS

vs

BAD ARABS

Minimum Temperature 45 Degrees Celsius. No Camels. No Subtitles.
Bring Your Own Ammo, Knives, Kebabs & Hummus.
Episode 1: Syria. Episode 2: Libya. Episode 3: Iraq.
Sponsored by Evian & Euro Arms Dealers.
Music by Maurice Hezbollah & The Muslim Brotherhood.

—

PAPERCRAFT LINDSAY LOHAN DOLL
WITH 8 REALISTIC ORIGAMI ORIFICES

—

Madeleine McCann

"IN CONCERT"
(Artist's Impression)

All Proceeds to a Charity. Sponsorship by Kleenex
Plus The Heartbreaking String Orchestra of Essex

A Faint Smell of Mould which on Closer Inspection Turns Out to be One of the Neighbours

—

"The 5 Top Chief Executive Officers To Watch 2005"
Dive Naked into a Pool of Investors

—

Political Realists Sing A Capella Jazz

Children's Crusade (Absolutely No Adults)

A Story About Timeless Sanity
Enacted by the Inmates of a Partially Modernised Asylum

LIKE FATHER LIKE SON

SYRIAN STREET THEATRE

Directed by Bashar al-Assad
Pre-Ramadan Opening Weekend in Hama, Deir Ezzor, Derra & Damascus
'99% ROTTEN' ON ROTTEN TOMATOES

—

Tea Party Special
Experimental Economic Opera

Standard & Poor Triple A Rating (t.b.c.).

No Sense. No Compromises.
Bring a Bottle, Gun & Mindless Ideology.
Founding Fathers Fancy Dress. Married Women Only. No Gays. No Lesbians. No Discounts for Welfare.

PLUS

The ABSOLUTE & FINAL
"Gamification of Poverty"

SEMI-DISPOSABLE WORKFORCE In NINE NEW FLAVOURS

—

DEBT NEGOTIATION FOR BEGINNERS
Pre-School Workshop

—

A Chorus of Illiterates Made to EAT WORDS

—

IN THE CAR PARK

A Fold-Away Bicycle Slalom Race
Between Businessmen in Suits Wearing Bike Helmets & Hi-Vis Jackets
Instead of Traffic Cones the Route is Marked
by a Series of Cowering Crouched Homeless Junkies Arranged in a Zig-Zag

PHILOSOPHICAL OBLIVION
ECONOMIC OBLIVION
INTELLECTUAL OBLIVION
MEDICAL OBLIVION
ETHICAL OBLIVION
RETAIL OBLIVION
REVOLUTIONARY OBLIVION
CONSENSUAL POLITICS OBLIVION
INERTIA OBLIVION
DEMOCRATIC OBLIVION
TECHNOLOGICAL OBLIVION
ALCOHOLIC OBLIVION
NARCOTIC OBLIVION
MORAL OBLIVION

PLUS OTHER OBLIVIONS t.b.c.

EGYPTIAN INTER-GENERATIONAL CAGE FIGHTING

feat.

HOSNI 'THE OCTOGENARIAN' MUBARAK (FATHER)

vs

ALAA 'THE BUSINESSMAN' & GAMAL 'THE MODERNISER' (SONS)

Winner Dies in Jail. Losers Get Hanged.

PLUS

THE WHITE TWATS
TEETH GRINDING ORCHESTRA

OF

ROTHERHAM

"MIAOW MIAOW / MEOW MEOW"
(PA / DJ SET)

THE COMPLETE EVAPORATION OF INVESTOR CONFIDENCE

Set to Esoteric Music from the Golden Age of New Age

PLUS

GLOBAL MARKETS IN FREEFALL 2011
An Ariel Ballet

Partly Inspired by 'GLOBAL MARKETS IN FREEFALL 2008'

Based on an original idea from 1929
Choreographed by Dow Jones. Everybody Welcome / Attendance Compulsory.

—

spirit-sappingly unfunny

COMEDY

HAND PICKED / 'FRESH' FROM LAST YEAR'S EDINBURGH

Inc. White Man with Gimmick / Black Man With Lisp / Limp Wrist & Posh Twat With Stolen Catchphrase
Chip On Shoulder: Biologically Female Double Act
Plus: Conceptual (Absolutely Not Funny) Comedy From Washington DC
& Hilarious Impersonation of Rural Accents, Mime of a Washing Machine, Masturbating Pensioners & Other Shit t.b.c.

"Idiots from Around the World" Dance Troupe 'Live' On Stage at 9.49

The End of the World

Starring David Cameron

Wearing a Vintage Action Man Frogman Outfit*
& Communicating via a Very Important Sat-Phone Link-Up

*Blue flippers, stick of dynamite, blue shorts, leg knife, speargun with spear, all in Good Condition

Set to Music by Michelle Obama &
A Man Who Claims to be Quentin Tarantino's Dope Dealer

PLUS

Asian Vegetable Markets in Turmoil

Morning Glory & Red Peppers Rot
Cucumbers Fall Off Stalls
Run on GM Cauliflowers / Beetroot Bundles Two for $1

—

In the Foyer

Men Blinded by Television

Women Bored to Death

Top Ten Tea Party Pundits
Drowned in a Bath
of their own Pig Ignorance, Malice & Spite

DEBT PANIC 3-D

Bring Your Own Glasses. Stereo Sound.

—

AMERICAN POLITICIANS & FINANCIERS DANCE NAKED CAP IN HAND TO 'CHINESE MUSIC'

EXHIBITION of FINANCIAL DERIVATIVES

Also feat. Derivative Paintings, Derivative Literature, Derivative Music, Derivative Haircuts

Social Justice at The Shopping Mall

"Looting is the Continuation of Politics by Other Means"

Summer Riot Season Kicks Off in London

Everything Must Go. Bring Your Own Petrol. Bring Your Own Shopping Trolley.
Costumes by Vivienne Westwood & Carl von Clausewitz

Highly Organised Teenagers

"Stolen Goods Slalom Challenge"

Contest Starts at Signal from Police Marksman

On The Big Stage

Community Spokesmen on Acid
Cops on Holiday
Commentators & Aging News Pundits on a 1980s Toxteth Nostalgia Trip

David Cameron's Animatronic Shirt

Reads a Short Pre-prepared Statement Explaining Why His Divisive Policies are Directly to Blame

AT DAWN
AGAINST THE SKY
SMOKE WRAITHS
DANCE
THE FORM
OF A LOGO
WHICH
DOES NOT
YET EXIST

PLUS

Community Opera
THE STENCH OF BURNING

SET TO NEW MUSIC BY JOE STRUMMER & VAUGHN WILLIAMS (DECEASED)
feat. "Tears in a Leftist's Eye". LYRICS BY THERESA MAY.
HYSTERICAL LAUGHTER BY MARGARENT THATCHER (sic).
NO COMMENT FROM CAMERON. DIRECTED BY SOCIAL MEDEA (sic).

**Light Chamber Music
&
the Test Card**

—

DAVID CAMERON'S HOLIDAY PHOTOGRAPHS

Illustrated Slide Show

—

Big Society

Masked Summer Ball
& Street Parties

**God Save The Queen
Land of Hope & Glory
We Are All In It Together**

On the Main Stage
FUCK THE POOR

Plus support t.b.c.

Looter Island / Reality TV

Introduced by Suspect Pundit & Haplessa Analysis
Music by Zack Dandy & The Hyperbole Orchestra

—

POSTCODE INFERNO
@ SW1A 2AA & SW1A 1AA

GUYS IN MASKS & GLOVES À LA MODE
TAKE RIOT TO THE PLACES
WHERE IT REALLY COUNTS

—

**NICK CLEGG, DAVID CAMERON
& ASSTD OTHER OLD ETONIANS
ARMED WITH CRICKET BATS, POLO STICKS & PAPER KNIVES
DEFEND DOWNING STREET IN PERSON
FROM BEHIND A BARRICADE OF TORY BULLSHIT**

Ringo Starr & Barbara Bach
Personally Clean Up Toxteth
Using Personalised Mops & Buckets

On The Daily Mail Main Stage

"DEATH TO THE UNACCEPTABLE"

Robust Execution of Jobless Looters

**Feat. a selection of Populist Punishments for Wayward Minors
Inc. Hanging, Lethal Injection & Starvation**
Lever Pulled by David Cameron

plus

SICK SOCIETY IN CONCERT

No Support

—

Pre-Olympic Warm Up Events

COLD BLOODED LIARS ON HOT BLOODY ICE

No Drunks. No Timewasters.

Eugenic Comedy Night
feat. Toxic Impressionist

David Starkey

"Underclass Accents & Patois from Around the World"

PLUS

David Cameron Discusses 'Black People' He Has Actually Talked To
Costumes by Adidas & Nike. Post Show Discussion Moderated using Matches & a Large Bottle of Petrol.

—

Quickfire Justice

Absurd & Exaggerated
Punishment Competition

Magistrates Only – Multiple Entries Welcome
Prizes Donated by News International

—

Launch of the Pre-School Prison Initiative
Inaugural Speeches by Robocop & a Man that once Punched Arnold Schwarzenegger

David Cameron's Super-Justice
More Just Than Actual Justice

MIDNIGHT EVICTION OF A WOMAN WHOSE BROTHER'S DOG ATE A LOOTED SAUSAGE

**Plus the Dog Itself Evicted from its Kennel
& then Fired from a Cannon Aimed Directly into a Lake of Fire
& the Dog's Puppies Put to Permanent Sleep using Adulterated Chemicals
& the Dog's Parents Shaved of Body Hair & Drowned in a Bucket of Sulphuric Acid**

Community Drama

Redemptive Stoning of a Minor Looter

Set to Music by Damon Eyebrow (sic) & Noel Gallagher

PLUS

David Cameron's Wagging Animatronic Finger

**A Choir of Privately Educated Children
Sing the Words of a Nine-Hour Lecture
Concerning Right & Wrong**

(Patois Translation by David Starkey)

—

**Rick Astley, Rick Perry & Ricky Martin Discuss
"What's In A Name?"**

Event Chaired by Ricky Gervais

NIGHT OLYMPICS
Watercannon Battles

Toxteth vs Tottenham
Birmingham vs Enfield
Gloucester vs Manchester
West Bromwich vs Birkenhead
Bristol vs Hackney
Haringey vs Lambeth
Islington vs Brixton
Croydon vs Streatham
Lewisham vs Ealing
Southwark vs Merton
Nottingham vs Peckham
Beckenham vs Bromley
Salford vs Oxford
Wolverhampton vs Birkenhead
Cardiff vs The Rest of the World
David Lammy vs David Starkey

Winner Stays On. Free Beer & Trainers.

PLUS

Special Pre-Dawn PLAYOFF Event
Turkish Guys with Kebab Knives

VS

Unspecified Looters

COMPULSORY NATIONWIDE MASS OUTDOOR STRIPTEASE

feat.

JOBLESS TROUBLEMAKERS, HOODIES & NO-PARENT FAMILIES

Judge's Decision is the Final Solution
Best Act Wins a Council House & 6 Months Remission

—

Cage Fighting
Men with Weak Knees

vs

Women with Weak Arguments

—

The New Great Fire of London
Set to Backwards Big Band Music

FRENZIED SELLING

plus

STRANGE GESTICULATIONS OF A RECENTLY SECTIONED STOCKBROKER
Set to Music by Jean Claude Van Damme's Dentist

—

MODERN LANGUAGES FOR BEGINNERS
Authoritarian Patois
Longwinded Legalese (American-English)
Pseudo-Streetspeak (TV Presenters / Intermediate Level Only)
Shit Talking for Shop Keepers

—

Exhibition of Young People Without University Places

Mindless Youth. Mindless Imprisonment. Mindless Rioting.
Mindless Nausea. Mindless Government. Mindless Debate.
Mindless Terror. Senseless Violence. Mindless Spinelessness.
Mindless Journalism. Mindless Destruction. Mindless Analysis.
Mindless Looting. Mindless Celebration. Mindless Commentary.
Mindless Justice. Mindless Nonsense. Mindless Policing.
Mindless Poverty. Mindless Vermin. Mindless Voting. Mindless Futility.
Mindless Beasts. Mindless Crap. Mindless People. Senseless People.
Mindless Sub-Humans. Senseless Children. Senseless Drivel.

Mindless Intelligence. Mindless Sentencing. Senseless Cops.
Senseless Cop Cars. Mindless Begging. Mindless Slavery.
Senseless Discipline. Senseless Logic. Senseless Stupidity.
Senseless Abjection. Senseless Sportswear. Mindless Punishment.
Mindless Poetry. Mindless Racism. Mindless Community.
Senseless Familes (sic). Mindless Idiocy. Senseless Vulgarity.
Mindless Parents. Mindless Discotheque. Mindless Alcohol.

Mindless Disgust. Mindless Animals. Mindless Teenagers.
Mindless Ideas. Mindless Vacancies. Senseless Empires.
Mindless Politics. Mindless Abuse. Mindless Scum.
Mindless Appetites. Senseless Indignity. Mindless Depravity.
Mindless Consumption. Mindless Excitement. Senseless Controversy.
Senseless Tear Gas. Mindless Infrastructure. Mindless Garbage.
Mindless Burning. Mindless Agony. Mindless Suffering.
Mindless Emptiness. Mindless Bullshit. Senseless Lies.
Mindless Shaming. Senseless Tragedy. Mindless Exaggeration.
Mindless Exploitation. Senseless Lunacy.
Mindless Senselessness. Senseless Mindlessness.

Hyper Visual
Single Mothers
with Low Self Esteem &
Hyper Active Children

ON ICE

plus

A Looking Glass Which Contains
Reflections of Things Which Are Not There

Battle of Professionals
Suicidal Clowns vs Hysterical Undertakers

No Exit by Jean Paul Satre (sic)

Additional Dialogue by Roman Polanski
Starring Muammar & Khamis Gaddafi
Set Design by NATO forward Air Controllers
Directed by No-One in Particular

IGNOBLE EXIT OF MUAMMAR GADDAFI

NO ENCORES. NO ENCORES REQUESTED.

NO APOLOGIES. NO REFUNDS.

PLUS

**INSANE
FULLY CIRCULAR
FULLY SELF-JUSTIFYING & SELF-CONTRADICTORY
COMMENTARY / ANALYSIS
BY MOUSSA IBRAHIM (LIBYAN GOVT. SPOKESMAN)**

COMING SOON

ALL NEW
LIBYAN
POWER
VACUUM

August 23 2011

THE INVISIBLE MAN

STARRING M. GADDAFI

SOUNDTRACK BY NATO BOMBARDMENT
CATERING BY THE RIXOS HOTEL IN TRIOPLI

A scientist dictator turns himself invisible <u>after facing sustained international criticism</u>. However, the potion he has taken drives him insane and he finds that he cannot become visible again, causing him to terrorize the countryside as an invisible killer. ~~People~~ Rebels etc search for him in ~~the mountainous region of Jebel Acacus, at the Atiq Mosque in Awjila, the Jabal Al Akdhar~~ area various hiding places in <u>Tripoli including a compound & a basement</u>. Just as the police accompany the attacked ~~maid~~ <u>population</u> back to their houses, the Invisible ~~Man~~ <u>Dictator</u> breaks in through the back door. Keeping his head cool, ~~Kemp~~ <u>the handsome rebel guy</u> bolts from the house and runs downhill to the ~~town~~ <u>oil wells</u> below, where he alerts a ~~navvy~~ <u>tribal elder</u> that the Invisible Man Dictator is approaching. The crowd in the town, witnessing the pursuit, rally around and when ~~Kemp~~ the handsome rebel guy is pinned down by ~~Griffin~~ <u>pro-Gaddafi forces</u>, the ~~navvy~~ <u>tribal elder</u> strikes him (?) with a spade and knocks him to the ground, and he is violently assaulted by the ~~workers~~ <u>guys from Benghazi</u>. ~~Kemp~~ <u>The handsome rebel guy</u> calls for the mob to stop, but it is too late. The Invisible ~~Man~~ <u>Dictator</u> dies of the injuries he has received, and his naked battered body slowly becomes visible on the ground after he dies. Later it is revealed that the invisibility formula is written in a mix of ~~Russian and Greek~~ <u>Arabic</u> which ~~Kemp~~ <u>NATO</u> cannot read, and with some pages washed out.

All Day & All Night Block Party

Bab al-Aziziya Compound

Bring An AK-47

Take Whatever You Want

PLEASE LEAVE THE PREMISES QUIETLY
& RESPECT OUR NEIGHBOURS
BY NOT MAKING UNNECESSARY NOISE

DJs MC Saif Houdini & Co.
Guest Choreography Coordinated by SAS Special Advisors

—

UK HIGH STREET
RECESSION BUSTER SPECIALS

Inc.

**Cut price Chemotherapy
Back Street Contortionists
Experimental Skin Grafts
& Other Specials t.b.c.**

Glasses That Are Only EVER Half Empty

&

Philosophy of Despair

—

M. Gaddafi & Sons Sing Good Old Songs of the Good Old Days

Pretty Much No Support. Secret Location t.b.c.

—

EFFIGIES OF GHOSTS FROM HISTORY

GOLD, BLOOD & VANITY PORTRAITS

DICTATOR
HOME DECOR
COURSE

Sponsored by Grazia

Special Guests M. Gaddafi (via Live by Satellite Link-Up) & Paris Hilton

No Snipers

—

WANNABE SUPERMODELS

MAKE LOVE TO THE CAMERA

—

'DOGFOOD' BURGERS
SERVED WITH
A MELANCHOLIC SAUCE

NOT FIT FOR HUMAN CONSUMPTION
CONTENTS MAY SETTLE DURING TRANSPORTATION

POLITICIANS IN PAINT

(Inc. Red, Blue & Yellow)

—

A Dream about Men with Symmetrical Faeces

—

Hurricane Irene 'In Concert'

plus

INTERPOL'S TOP TEN
IDENTICAL INSTANCES
OF IDENTITY FRAUD

LET NATURE TAKE ITS COURSE

A LARGE SCALE SITE–SPECIFIC AMERICAN WATER BALLET INSPIRED BY JUDGEMENT DAY

Audience Evacuated Free of Charge. Rescue Workers' Costumes by Marc Jacobs & John Galliano.
Music by John Cage (deceased) in collaboration with Harry Gregson-Williams. Vocals by Dolly Parton & Kanye West.

plus

ALL AMERICA

OUTDOOR WET T-SHIRT CONTEST (FINALS)

Venue: Rikers Island. Prizes presented by Kate Upton & Mayor Bloomberg.
ALL CONTESTANTS GET A SIGNED PICTURE OF ROBERTO ARANGO'S ASSHOLE

PARTIALLY SYNCHRONISED NATIONWIDE POWER CUTS

Deepest Longest Darkness Wins a Prize

—

Rendition of the Weathermen

—

Best of Internet Hurricane Deaths

Inc. Man Struck by Billboard, Woman Blown Into Mincer, Dog on a Wet Tin Roof etc.

—

MONTE CARLO DEHYDRATION FESTIVAL

headliner SIR TOM JONES
plus support from BUPA

LIVE
ULTRASOUND

BEYONCÉ'S
FOETUS
EXCLUSIVE

Plus Other Leaked Celebrity Medical Scans Inc. MRI of a famous golfer,
Lumbar Puncture of an Astronaut, Kidney Cam of a Pre-Teen Syrian Model etc.

The Law of Diminishing Returns

Plus other Laws
Inc. Sod's Law & Murphy's Law
The Law of the Jungle
The Law of the Playground
The Law of the Morgue
The Law of the Shotgun
The Law of the Lottery Rollover
The Law of the Graveyard
The Law of the Car Park
& The Law of the Call Centre

—

'LIVE' IN THE BASEMENT

The Growing Unreliability of a Suspect
After Months of Torture & 'Hard' Interrogation

Directed by a Bloke that Went to Harrow & Enacted by 5 Former Footballers Turned Thespians
Partially Original Soundtrack by Craig Dandruff & Victoria Scheiss-Colon

Dancing for Dinner

An Old Man on the Brink of
Hopeless Starvation
Performs
Degrading & Clumsy
Pirouettes
on the Brink of a Pavement
to Great Hilarity
of Sundry Teenagers
who Throw Chips at Him
& Applaud

—

World Markets Rally

A DERIVATIVE SYMPHONY
DEPICTING ECONOMIC OBLIVION
PLAYED ON A XYLOPHONE
MADE FROM RECYCLED COMPUTER
& LAWNMOWER PARTS

No Latecomers

Contents May Settle During Transportation to the Penal Colonies

Members of the Gaddafi Family

APPEAR & DISAPPEAR
APPARENTLY AT WILL

Making Deluded Speeches
& Declaring their Intentions
to Either Make Peace or War

Not Suitable for Children

The Performance Uses Strobe Lighting, Smoke, Gunshots, Fireworks, Loud Bangs, Bad Language & Nudity
May Contain Systematic Racist Violence against Black Libyans & Migrants from sub-Saharan Africa
Bring Your Own Drinking Water, Guns & Aummunition (sic). Bring Your Own Polling Stations. Bring Your Own Constitution

—

'WHAT'S LEFT OF THE HEALTH SERVICE' FIGHT NIGHT

Toothless Shaking Old Men
in Baseball Caps

vs

Witless Trembling & Incontinent Old Women
in Stretch Lycra

Win Free Laser Surgery, M.R.I. Scans, Medication & Health Supplements
Prizes Presented by Andrew Lansley's Next Door Neighbour
Partially Supported by the B.M.A.

—

"GORDIAN KNOT"

PANEL DISCUSSION OF INTELLECTUAL OCTOPUSES

Unreality TV

"BIG BROTHER ACID HOUSE" FORMER CONTESTANTS ON POWERFUL HALLUCINOGENS

Inc. Jade Goody (Deceased), "Brian" Belo & Sophie Reade

—

Statistics Brought to Life in a Delightful & Partially Intriguing Finger Puppet Show

Music by the Drummer from a Van Halen Tribute Band

—

TRIVIA QUIZ
Educated Idiots

VS

Idiotic Educators
Win a Monthly Subscription to the Internet

INTERNATIONAL TOP TEN RACIST FOOTBALL SONGS

Inc.
A CHORUS OF BULGARIAN MONKEY CHANTS

—

In the Basement

INHUMAN REMAINS

—

Fantasy Cabaret

SOMEONE WHO IS NOT RUPERT MURDOCH
JERKS OFF ON THE FEET OF SOMEONE
WHO IS NOT REBEKAH BROOKS

CHEMICAL HOMESICKNESS

plus

ABSTRACT PATTERNS
WHICH PRODUCE
A FEELING
OF NAUSEA

—

Northern Hemisphere Premiere

Re-scheduled from Previously Arranged Date

Best Administrative Errors 2010 / 2011

Set to Music by Mr. Randy Numan (sic)

Performance Begins 30 minutes Late to Allow Dancers to Arrive from a Prior Engagement
Green Ticket Holders are Requested to Sit in the Orange Seating Zone
Audio Description in French ONLY
No Disabled Access. No Dogs including Guide Dogs.
No Coat Check, Refreshments or Bathroom Facilities in the Building

"ALL PUNISHMENT ALL OF THE TIME"

DAVID CAMERON'S MORAL EDU-TAINMENT PANOPTICAL NEO-VICTORIAN GULAG

86,821 NEW GOVT. SPONSORED DIGITAL PRISON-TV CHANNELS feat. LIVE SHAME & INCARCERATION OF ALL UK OFFENDERS

Inc. Court Cams, Judgement Cams, Solitary Cams & Prison-Van Cams
Grown Men Weeping in their Cells / Best Homemade Tattoos of E-Wing
Free Hand-Jobs for Lifers & Tough Love for Grasses PLUS Dope, Whisky (sic) & Smuggled Mobiles

Operatic Poverty

&

Rendition to Torture

—

Amateur Theatre
Mall Security Guards, Parking Wardens
& Railway 'Revenue Protection' Officers

present

Jobsworth's Inferno

Strobe Lighting. Smoke Effects. Partial Modern Dress.

Best of Looter Videos #1
Inc. 'Me & Naz', 'New Shorts', 'Boots Crash & Grab'
& 'Feral Firestarters of Tottenham'

FISCAL BOTOX

plus

**International Cancer of the Gold Reserves
& Economic Leukaemia**

—

SEMI-LEGAL TIMESHARE

—

New Nine-Part Drama

Insurance Related Arson
of an Almost Derelict Spoon Factory

—

FIGHT NIGHT IN THE PAY & DISPLAY CAR PARK

FAT & POOR

vs

RICH & THIN

WIN A VISIT TO THE DENTIST

Statistical Analysis
Statistical Massage
Statistical Murder
Statistical Justice
Statistical Poverty
Statistical Fiction
Statistical Innumeracy
Statistical Weight Loss
Statistical Unpleasantness
Statistical Manipulation
Statistical Magic
Statistical Bullshit
Statistical Bloodbath
Statistical Boredom
Statistical Numbers
Statistical Impoverishment
Statistical Racism
Statistical Science
Statistical Sarcasm
Statistical Errors
Statistical Voodoo
Statistical Vitality
Statistical Intelligence
Statistical Discrimination
Statistical Collagen
Statistical Divorces
Statistical Palliatives
Statistical Pain Thresholds

Plus other violence, to be confirmed.

A Ballet
of Bomb Sweeps,
Dog Patrols
& Bag Searches

Also feat. Hi-Tech Surveillance of Tunnels & Bridges & a Chorus of Soldiers Operating Vehicle Checkpoints

—

Concert of Pre-Anniversary Tears

All Proceeds to Ground Zero Property Developers

Slow Motion Memories Set to Stomach Punching Music
by Barry Rachmaninov & Sergei Boxcutter

PLUS

"Idiotic Movie Night"

WTC Claymation 3D
Music by The Rockstars of Grief

Guatanomo (sic) Sunset
Buddy Movie About Two Interrogators

Extraordinary Rendition of an Idiot
Extraordinary Rendition of an Innocent

Plus Other Movies t.b.c.

9.11: AERIAL BALLET

10th Anniversary Re-Staging of the Controversial Work the 2001 Premiere of which Ended in Tragedy

Music by George Gershwin (Deceased)
Long Video by Andy Warhol (Deceased)

All New Epic Drama

"Slave Drivers of Leighton Buzzard"

(PG Cert.)

—

Memory Porn
Disaster Porn
Terror Porn
Liberation Porn
Vengeance Porn
Torture Porn
Boredom Porn

—

SINGALONG-A-SONG CONTEST

Songs about Men with no Morals

vs

Songs about Women with no Clothes

PROPOSAL
FOR AN ARSON–BASED
REFORM OF
THE BANKING SYSTEM

plus

SIX STRICTLY SCIENTIFIC
EXPERIMENTS
IN MAKING MATTERS
WORSE

—

ANGER MANAGEMENT WORKSHOP

PIE EATING CONTEST

PLUS

HOPELESS FILTHY DOLE SCROUNGERS
BATHED IN GROSS DOMESTIC PRODUCT

—

Men who Look Increasingly Concerned Make Various Announcements to the Effect That Everything in Kabul is Under Control
Intermittent Translation. Irrelevant Commentary.

—

New Perfume Product Launch
Servile Evasiveness

DOLE POPS CHALLENGE / NO HIT WONDERS

SIMON COWELL & JAMIE OLIVIER (sic) FORM POP GROUPS OF THE YOUTH UNEMPLOYED

FREE FINALE CONCERT feat. 972,000 'TALENTED YOUNG PEOPLE'
DIVIDED INTO 121,500 QUARTETS, 20249 TRIOS, 212,626 DUOS & ONE SOLOIST
Sponsored by The Nationalist Lottery. Outfits by Madame Tusaudes (sic) & Madame Jo Jo's.
Presented by Daniel Craig & Pierced Brosnan (no relation). Filmed Undercover by BBC.

—

WHIST DRIVE
AUSTERITY DRIVE
BEETLE DRIVE

HAMMER UNSANITARY HOUSE OF HORROR DOUBLE BILL
MATERIALISM IN GENERAL (X Cert.)
&
TOXIC FRATERNITY OF THE BOURGEOISIE
(Based on a Book but ADAPTED BY A TOTAL FUCKING IDIOT)

LIVE FROM BENGHAZI

DAVID CAMERON MAKES
A NINE-HOUR SPEECH
EXPLAINING WHY HE HAS QUIT
AS PRIME MINISTER
OF ENGLAND
TO BECOME
THE NEW KING OF LIBYA

PLUS OTHER SIMILAR SPEECHES BY NICHOLAS SARKOZY

—

RECORD BREAKING ROGUE TRADERS
PRESENT TEN TOP TRICKS & TIPS
FOR LOSING OTHER PEOPLE'S MONEY

Special Guests: Jerome Kerviel (Société Générale), Nick Leeson (Barings) & introducing Kweku Adoboli (U.B.S.)

WHICH TASER?

GET the
MOST VOLTAGE
FOR your
MONEY

With reps from Avon & Somerset, Devon & Cornwall, Gwent, Lincolnshire, Merseyside, Metropolitan Police, Northamptonshire, Northumbria, North Wales & West Yorkshire Police Forces

"MORE VOLTAGE
MEANS
MORE ENFORCEMENT"

Special Seminar #1: Tasering A Kid
Special Seminar #2: Tasering A Rabbit
Special Seminar #3: Tasering an Idiot
Special Seminar #4: Tasering an Octegenerian (sic)

TRAINEE OLYMPIANS RUNNING IN CIRCLES AT EXACTLY THE RATE OF INFLATION

VS

AEROBICS-MINDED DRUNKEN STUDENTS RUNNING AT A SPEED ROUGHLY IN LINE WITH THE RETAIL PRICE INDEX

FREE FOOD

Inc.
Filthy Dog–Meat Kebabs & Mushy Peas
with Deep Fried Razor Blades
in a Batter of Sand, Sump Oil & Floor Scrapings

THE INANE & SHAMEFUL WIRETAPPED BOASTING OF SILVIO BERLUSCONI SET TO A DISCO SOUNDTRACK

Inc. the classics '11 Women In A Bed', 'Abuse of Power', 'Freedom People'
& the Beach Club Party Sensation 'Part-Time Prime Minister'
Backing Vocals by a Bathtub Full of Big Brother Contestants,
Chorus Dancers & Beauty Contest Wannabes

FREE FOOD

Spermicidal Pot Noodle & Dry Bread ETF.s
Hidden in a Basket of Investments Intended to Mimic a Market's Movements
May Cause Indigestion. May Contain Traces of Nuts & Other Allergens.

—

LATE NIGHT DEBATE ON THE PATIO
HAPLESS MATERIALISTS
vs
HOPELESS CONSUMERISTS

Foyer Bar Promotion

NOW UNDER NEW MISMANAGEMENT

COCKTAIL MENU / UNHAPPY HOUR

'Eight Drinks for the Price of Eleven'

The Crash of 08/09
Potato Vodka, Diet Sprite, Liquified Deodorant

The Crash of 29
Bathtub Gin, Muscle Relaxants, Non-Silicon Breast Milk

Toxic Loan
Jack Daniels, Rohypnol, Anti-Caking Agent

The Bad Debt
Jim Beam, Blood Sugar, GM Stinging Nettles

Fall of the Nikkei
Sake, Liquid Ether, Dry Ice, Mistress Tears

Rogue Trader
Brandy, Black Sugar, Astroturf, Masculine Sweat

Eurozone Sour
Tequila, Urine, Lime Juice, Adrenaline

Blind Panic
Absinthe, Pocket Dust, Galliano, Ejaculate, Windscreen Condensation

Road to Recovery
Tap Water, Tumbleweed, Severance & Moonshine

September 21 2011

All Night
(Strictly Limited Run)

Temporarily Live in Concert

Troy Davis

One Man Show

Shame of Georgia
Shame of The Georgia Board of Pardons and Paroles
Shame of America
Shame of Justice
Shame of the Courts
Shame of the System
Shame of Madison MacPhail
Shame of the Cops
Shame of the Law

With Music by
Brewer and Shipley
Gladys Knight and the Pipps
Vicki Lawrence
Charley Daniels
& Ray Charles

NARCISSISTS IN A HOUSE WITH NO MIRRORS*

(*or other reflective surfaces)

—

PANEL DISCUSSION

MURDERING SLEEP

State Executioners from China, Iran, Iraq, the United States, Pakistan & Burma Discuss What They Do To Relax

Feat. Top Ten Tips on How to Eliminate Conscience & How to Sleep Easy in Your Bed at Night

Discussion Chaired by Troy Davis (Deceased)

With contributions from Abdul Hamid bin Hussain bin Moustafa al-Fakki (Deceased) & Junior presenter Alireza Molla-Soltani (Deceased)

Sponsored by The Georgia Board of Pardons and Paroles

EROTIC DANCE OF LARGELY DESTITUTE PAUPERS

Their Nakedness Partially Shrouded by a Confusing Fog of Inflation, Tax Rises & Real-Terms Benefit Cuts

Choreographed by Pina Bausch (DECEASED)

With Music by R.E.M.

HIGH JUMP CONTEST

AMATEUR ATHLETES

VS

ANIMATRONIC ANTELOPES

CONTESTANTS LEAP BLINDFOLDED OVER A ROPE
HELD BETWEEN LADDERS THAT WERE TAKEN
FROM A BUILDER THAT WENT OUT OF BUSINESS

**No Drunks. No Shoes with Springs in Them.
Protective Headgear Essential**

—

All New & Partially Original

Common Sense Deniers /
U.N. Chronic-Compulsive
Political Deafness
Convention

Special Guests t.b.c.

THE DARK NIGHT RETURNS

VLADIMIR PUTIN FOREVER

ALL NEW CONSTITUTION–DODGING RUSSIAN–JOB–SWAP REALITY–TV

With repeat performance from DMITERY MADOVEDEV (sic)
Official Sponsors: Mafia / K.G.B.

PLUS

Italian Comi-Cabaret with Hilarious Controversial Duo

Standards & Poor

Pay to Get Out. Euros Not Accepted.

CAGE FIGHT

Teens
vs
Toddlers

Undiscovered Geniuses
vs
Unreconstructed Chauvinists

Taliban in Exploding Turbans
vs
Gnarly Bikers in Safety Compliant Headgear

PLUS

Partially Trained Celebrities
Tightrope Walk
Over a Deep Pit
Filled with a Starving
Crack-Addicted Underclass

REVERSE DIRECTION FINANCE AWARDS

Top Ten
Best International
Unsustainable Business Models

Win a DESK, a STORAGE CUBICLE & a CALCULATOR

—

PARTIALLY AMAZONIAN
FLUTE MUSIC
FOR ELEVATORS

'LIVE CONCERT'

WITH SPECIAL CONTRIBUTION
BY 15 AMERICAN TOURISTS
WEARING PONCHOS

—

Terminal Rises in the Cost of Living

Best of Internet Self-Immolation #2

Inc. Buddhist Priests, Defective Molotov Protestor, Superhero Impersonators etc.

A
VERY
DIFFICULT
SITUATION
INDEED

DRAMATISED
IN SEVERAL
PARTS

WITH ORIGINAL MUSIC BY ANGELA MERKE (sic)
& THE ONGOING WALL STREET OCCUPATION ORCHESTRA
LIGHTING FX BY THE I.M.F.

FREE TIMESHARE KEBAB HOUSE, OUZO RESTAURANT & RECYCLED PIZZA

Dante's

Tevez in Purgatory

A Long Boring Opera
About a Footballer Sentenced to the Substitutes Bench
For Eternity or Until Death Whichever is the Longer

Music by The Saturdays in collaboration with
Michael Nyman's Central Heating Engineer

—

SAUDI LADIES SUNDAY DRIVING CLUB
MEETING CANCELLED UNTIL FURTHER NOTICE

LIVE ON STAGE

THE NATION'S HIGHEST EARNERS URINATE FROM A GREAT HEIGHT INTO THE OPEN MOUTHS OF ITS POOREST FAMILIES

Ladders provided by a recently Bankrupted D.I.Y. Store

Free Drink of Water For All Contestants
No Gargling

—

Remote Control Teenagers Set A Good Example for Others

Batteries Not Included

EVIL LIVE / DEMONIC MUSIC

Medieval Attitudes Tour

AMANDA KNOX
THE DOUBLE SOUL
IN CONCERT

Inc. songs from her album 'Enchanting Witch'
Concert & Post-Gig Transportation Arranged by 'A U.S. television Network'
Catering, Costumes, Theatrics & Legal Incompetence Kindly Provided by the town of Perugia

—

ALL THE FUN OF THE ARMS FAIR

"DRONE STRIKE CHALLENGE"

INTERNATIONAL CONTESTANTS HIDE
FROM 'TELE–OPERATED JUSTICE WEAPONRY'
American Citizens Welcome. Prizes Presented by Anwar al-Awlaki (Deceased).

A Goode
Olde Fashioned
Heatwave

feat. Music by Ludicrous Sunburn & Sergio Ringtone
800,000 Litres of Non-E.U. Standard Complimentary Ice Cream
Provided by Lord Mayor of London
(Suntan Lotion, GM Strawberry & Spermicide Flavour Only)

plus

Recession-Buster
Slap-Up Specials

Roast Ox & a Packet of Crisps
Chicken Legs From Concentrate
Linda MCarteney's (sic) Vegetarian Surprise

Single Dads, Crack Heads & War Veterans Eat Free. (Terms & Conditions May Apply.)

—

Fully Modernised Roundabouts &
Futuristic Amusement Arcades

Top speed 200mph. May cause headaches, nosebleeds & nausea.

October 3 2011

Wall Street /
Woodstock

DIRECTED BY OLIVER STONE & MICHAEL WADLEIGH

A young and impatient ~~stockbroker~~ <u>protester</u> is willing to do anything to <u>stop</u> ~~get to the top, including trading on illegal inside information taken through~~ a ruthless and greedy corporate <u>capitalism</u> ~~raider who takes the youth under his wing.~~ An intimate look at the ~~Woodstock Music & Art Festival held in Bethel, NY in 1969,~~ <u>Wall Street protest</u> from preparation through cleanup, with historic access to insiders, blistering concert footage, and portraits of the ~~concertgoers~~ <u>protesters</u>; negative and positive aspects are shown, from drug use by ~~performers~~ <u>investment bankers</u> to naked ~~fans~~ <u>hedge fund managers</u> sliding in the mud, from the collapse of the ~~fences~~ <u>banks</u> by the 'unexpected' <u>downturn</u> ~~hordes~~ to the surreal arrival of National Guard helicopters laden with with <u>Mace</u> ~~food~~ and ~~medical assistance~~ <u>arrest warrants</u> for the impromptu city of 500,~~000~~.

—

plus

STRATEGY SEMINAR

JPMorgan Chase
"Purchasing Justice"

City Police Force As Private Security & Other $4.6 Million Dollar Low Points in Ethics of Charitable Donation
Adults Only. Free Laptop & Security Monitoring Software. No Drummers. No Jugglers. No Face Painters. No Free Runners. etc.

HEAD-BURSTING LECTURE BY A MAN WHOSE BLOOD PRESSURE IS EXPONENTIALLY INVERSELY LINKED TO THE STRENGTH OF THE GREEK ECONOMY

—

My Book Deal Ordeal
Amanda Knox

Ghostwritten by Meredith Kercher
With additional, confusing, logically inconsistent & alternate reality material by Rudy Guede
Tasteful Pictures by David LaChapelle & Terry Richardson

Mountains of Old Contaminated Evidence
& Medeavil (sic) Rhetoric by Legal System of Perugia

—

GENUINE ROMANY
TOXIC KARMIC BALANCING
WITH SEMI-LEGAL CREDIT TEASING

NIGHT SO THICK
IT TAKES ON
THE APPEARANCE
OF A SOLID OBJECT

feat. Music by Dead People

—

A Ballet of Drugged Rats in A Vast Temporary Lab Maze

Spiteful Early Christmas Presents

Rectilinear Structures
Whose Purpose is Hard to Identify

—

Rich / White & Privileged Idiots
Dancing to Music
That They Do Not & Will Not Ever
Understand

New Madchester
After Ecstasy; the Reaper

"Promises of Sugared Poison"

feat. David Cameron & Co.

—

Human Rights Are Slowing the Economy /

Compulsory Common Sensification for Idiots

—

Raving Lunatic Head Boy Speeches of Old Eton Vol. 9.
& Suspect Schizo–Optimism & Delusional Fighter Rhetoric

—

In The Basement
'Secret Gig'

Dr. Death & His Harsh Medicine
with chorus of cheering BUPA Reps
& personal appearance by Rip Van Winkle

STEVE JOBS' LIFE IN BILL GATES' WORDS

AS TOLD TO Charles Babbage & ALAN TURING (Deceased)

—

Chinese Workers 'Impromptu' Assembly Line Salute

NINE-HOUR CELEBRATION OF LAZINESS

—

ON THE 'CARLSBERG BIG SCREEN' IN 'THE TIMEWARNERAOL CARPARK'
"SLOPPY SECONDS / OLD STONE TO NEW BUILDING"

Stunning Innovators of Chart Music
Improve Contemporary Dance by Giving it More Beatz

Fair Game. 'Fair Use'. Fuck Off.

feat.

William Forsyth served a la Nicole Scherzinger
Christina Aguilera grinds her CREATIVE crotch all over Steve Paxton
Shakira SHOOTS HER ARTISTIC LOAD into Merce Cunningham (Deceased)
Leona Lewis SHAKES it RAW like Meg Stuart
Jennifer Lopez funks the shit out of Pina Bausch
Beyoncé beats it to the BANK with Anne Teresa De Keersmaeker

PLUS

APPROPRIATION COUNTERATTACK BY JEROME BEL

—

Apple Macintosh Colouring Competition
8 Outline Pictures of an Assembly Line to Colour in at Home
Win Workers' Rights, Health Insurance & an iPad

MICHAEL JACKSON GLOVE PUPPET AUTOPSY TRIBUTE

WITH 3T, ALEXANDRA BURKE, ALIEN ANT FARM, BEYONCÉ*, CEE LO GREEN, CHRISTINA AGUILERA, CRAIG DAVID, DIVERSITY & GLADYS KNIGHT AS THE BUNGLING AUTOPSY TEAM

(*as Anne Teresa De Keersmaeker)

PLUS

Music by JACKSON BROTHERS
LATOYA JACKSON
& Other Jacksons t.b.c.

—

APPLE'S MARKET SHARE IN THE AFTERLIFE

Panel Discussion & Painfully Extended
Esoteric Speculative Analysis by Financial Idiots

Sounds That Set Your Teeth On Edge

—

In the Abandoned Annex

Hallucinatory Sports Assoc.

Shadow Boxing For Glue Sniffers

Contests Conducted by Torchlight. Winners Go Free.
Losers Enter a Depressing & Destructive Spiral of Institutional Care

The Delirium Tremens Orchestra

Theme Tune to Rambo & other Theme Tunes t.b.c.

—

David Cameron's
British History Citizenship Pub Quiz

Ten Pointless Facts About England Wins A Passport
Three Wrong Answers & You're Deported
Five Wrong Answers & You're Hooded, Beaten & Rendered for Torture in Pakistan

—

Liam Fox & Adam Werritty
in a series of Apparently Spontaneous Meetings with Businessmen All over the World
NB: Not For Profit

On the Grozny 'Avarice' Floating Stage

Hilary Swank &
Jean-Claude van Damme

EAT THE UNSEASONED SHIT
OF Pres. RAMZAN KADYROV
OUT OF BOWLS
MADE FROM THE SKULLS
OF HUMAN RIGHTS CAMPAIGNERS

$1000 Per Mouthful @ Av. 400 Mouthfuls Per Serving

WITH MUSICAL ACCOMPENIAMENT (sic) BY VANESSA MAE

—

Child Poverty Discotheque

NOW WITH INCREASED CAPACITY OF 600,000.
No Crèche. No Heating.

NO WAY OUT

ALL WEEK

Freeze (sic) Art Fair
'The Best of The Worst'

Special Projects by
SauerKraut & Colonial
Yarbble Bagman
Minter Trustfund
& Ecoli Collective

plus

ABSOLUT DESTITUTE LONDON
city-wide installation
Produced by Coalition Govt. Sponsored by Smirinoff (sic), Stolichnaya & Zubrowka.

SECONDARY MARKET / RECORD-BREAKING PRICES
Heironymus Bosch 'Jobseekers in Hell'
Pablo Picasso 'Privatized Guernica'
Jeff Koons 'Inflatable Poverty'
&
Partially Exclusive Jasper Johns Semi-Limited Print Edition
'Bloody Flags / Body Bags'

—

All New Marquis de Sade Incomplete Manuscripts
'The 120 Days of Saddam'

Imaginary Concentration Camp Architecture: 1st International Prize
Live & Lengthy Jury Deliberations with Eventual Announcement of Predictable Results
No Translation

British Jobless
British Torture
British Racists
British Timekeeping
British Ignorance
British Slavery
British Poverty
British Custard
British Justice
British Mud
British Sex
British Idiots
British Bureaucrats
British Dentistry
British Obesity
British Tolerance
British Knife Attacks
British Hooligans
British Illnesses
British PowerPoint
British Petroleum
British Bombast
British Lies
British Armies
British Sadness
British Chemicals
British Class System
British Paedophiles
British Xenophobes
British Flags
British Babes
British Brains
British Shit
British Cock
British Balls
British Memory
British Forgetting

British Bulldogs
British Bikers
British Cat-Flaps
British Pensions
British Museums
British Robots
British Ravers
British Rastas
British Muslims
British Savages
British Inbreeding
British Terror
British Toxins
British Shambles
British Rescue Parties
British Pigs
British Bacon
British Beef
British Bullies
British Trade
British Science
British Sarcasm
British Holidays
British Dance Music
British Traffic Wardens
British Eccentrics
British Football
British Whores
British Rent Boys
British Rent Collectors
British Kitsch
British Strippers
British Shit-Stirrers
British Codswallop
British Chemicals
British Gravediggers
British Idiots
British Sheep
British Sorrow
British Privilege

MICHAEL JACKSON
(DECEASED)

&

BERTOLT BRECHT
(DECEASED)

VISIT

OCCUPY ROTHERHAM

TO TALK, INSPIRE & ENTERTAIN THE CROWDS

ALSO FEAT. GAMELAN / DRUMMING WORKSHOP
& A CURIOUS BOOK SIGNING APPEARANCE BY HIS ROYAL HIGHNESS JULIAN ASSANGE

—

STEVE JOBS IMPERSONATORS
"Product Launch Karaoke Contest"

Winner Stays On. Win an iPod or Equivalent.
Prizes presented by Stephen Fry's Therapist

CUTTING EDGES / CRUEL HUMOUR
ALL Night Compulsory Stand-up

**Open Mic. For Torturers, Morons, Idiots & Sadists
Inc. Material from The I.S.I. Jokebook & Manual of Waterboarding Humour etc.**

—

AN INTERNATIONAL SELECTION
OF WELL PAID POLITICAL LOBBYISTS,
THEIR WIVES, MISTRESSES & CHILDREN
LAUNCHED INTO A VACUUM CHAMBER
WITHOUT PROTECTIVE CLOTHING
OR BREATHING EQUIPMENT

Not Suitable For Faint Hearted Humanists or Children
Music by Sonic Youth. Guest Vocals by Barry Manilow.

—

SELF–SERVING IDIOTS'
SELF–SERVICE CAFETERIA

FREE can of Coke & Crisps with every purchase. Effluent & Gum Disease Flavour Only.

PAINTING BY JOBLESS NUMBERS: GIGANTIC BLEAK PICTURE OF ENGLAND PAINTED BY WORKLESS PROLES

Bring Your Own Brushes, Overalls & Paints

—

Bookies Delight / CORRUPT SPORTS DAY

FIXED CRICKET & BOXING MATCHES
FIXED FOOTBALL MATCHES
FIXED HORSE & SWIMMING RACES

Refereed, judged & otherwise adjudicated by an INTERNATIONAL GROUP of CORRUPT OFFICIALS

All Bribes Payable Fully on Entrance

HILARIOUS
ONE-MAN SHOW

ALL THE WAY FROM DUBAI

ANDREW 'Not For Profit' WERRITTY

in

PERSISTENT IMPERSONATION OF A GOVT. EMPLOYEE

Free Admittance for Dr. Liam Fox & Co.

—

INFLATION INFLATION INFLATION

'5.2% NEW TV SHOW'

WIN A SUITCASE / PRAM / TROLLEY OVERFLOWING WITH WORTHLESS CURRENCY
EVERYONE WELCOME / COMPULSTORY (sic) PARTICIPATION

Ticket Prices Variable

plus

FINANCIAL PRODUCT LAUNCH
SANTANDER SAVINGS SHRINKER

With speeches by Michael Caine & Kenneth Williams (Deceased)

ECONOMIC HEAD TRAUMA

—

ESCALATORS THAT GO DOWN FOREVER

—

DALE FARM ELECTRO-ACOUSTIC ORCHESTRA

SYMPHONY FOR TASER, DEFIBRILATOR, DRUM, YELL & FLAME

Commissioned by Basildon Council & Essex Police

ALL NEW LIBYAN JUSTICE
& INTERNATIONALLY SPONSORED DUE PROCESS

ONE
IN THE
HEAD
ONE
IN THE
STOMACH
TWO
IN THE
KNEES

MOBILE PHONE PICTURES OF THE DEAD

—

OBJECTS FROM WHICH THE SOUND HAS BEEN REMOVED

PERSONS FROM WHOM THE VOICES HAVE BEEN REMOVED

& etc.

—

Free Market Seminar
OUTSOURCING CONSCIENCE

GRAND PARADE

PEOPLE WHOSE NAMES HAVE BEEN REMOVED

PEOPLE WHOSE POSSESSIONS HAVE BEEN CONFISCATED

PEOPLE WHOSE IDENTITIES HAVE BEEN STOLEN

PEOPLE WHOSE FACES HAVE BEEN PARALYSED

WORDS WHOSE MEANINGS HAVE BEEN DESTROYED

SONGS WHOSE TUNES HAVE BEEN ERADICATED

BOOKS WHOSE WORDS HAVE BEEN ERASED

STORIES WHOSE MEANING HAS BEEN FORGOTTEN

PLUS

GENERALISED NOISE

A RAINBOW PAINTED IN SEVEN SHADES OF BLOOD

—

'HISTORICAL' EXHIBIT

THE BODY OF A TYRANT, BRUTALISED & LEFT TO ROT DISPLAYED IN A WALK-IN DEEP FREEZE

Free Entrance & David Cameron's Home Made Ice Cream. Children Welcome.
Bring Your Own Nose-Clip. Democrats & Freedom Lovers Only.
Absolutely Last Chance. Show MUST CLOSE SATURDAY before TOTAL PUTRIFICATION.

Next Week: Margaret Thatcher

LETHARGIC WRESTLING

SMACK HEADS
VS
DEMORALISED PENSIONERS

TEENS ON PRESCRIPTION TRANQUILISERS
VS
APATHETIC PRISONERS

Win a Half-Bottle of Champagne or Equivalent
Prizes presented by Carla Bruni's Next Door Neighbour

—

FAST TRACK TO SCRAPHEAP

Three-Legged Race Between Finance Ministers & Bankers from Greece, Irish Republic & Portugal, their Legs BOUND TOGETHER Using Innovative JAPANESE Fabrics & Vermin Ligaments

CERTIFIED SLUMP OIL

COMPLETE IMMEDIATE & ABSOLUTE MARKET RECOVERY GUARANTEED OR 'YOUR' 'MONEY' 'BACK'

COLD WATER ON HOPES OF RECOVERY

A BOOTLEG HOLOGRAM OF JOHN DENVER

DEATH BY ECONOMIC LIPOSUCTION

REANIMATION OF A RENTED GONDOLA

—

CHILD LABOUR WEEK

HALF-SIZE PORTIONS. EVERYTHING HALF PRICE.

—

Lunchtime Entertainment for the EuroZone Crisis Meeting

feat. Bored Non-Schengen Strippers & a Blind Comedian. Cold Snacks of Reconstituted Currywurst.

INTERNATIONAL THEATRE OF MONEY

More Shits-Inducing / Boring Adventures With Predictable Highs & Tedious Lows

Starring the U.S. Dollar, the Yen, Pounds Sterling & the Euro
Inc. Special Guest Appearance by the Zloty & the Kuna

—

Who Killed Gaddafi?

Totally Half-Hearted Enquiry
feat. Team of Unpaid & Disinterested Investigators
'We Swear that Culprit will be Told Off & Allowed to Escape'

—

Greek Gods Return

To Wreak Vengeance on International Bankers

feat. Cast in Approximate Alphabetical Order:
Aphrodite, Apollo, Ares, Artemis, Athena, Demeter,
Dionysus, Hades, Hera, Hephaestus, Hermes, Hestia, Poseidon & Zeus.

Not Suitable for Workers in the Financial Sector.
Special Effects by Ray Harryhausen.

THERMAL IMAGES OF HOMELESS PEOPLE

(VERY COLOURFUL / VERY AESTHETIC)

—

ALL EUROPE
TOP TEN
PREMATURE SEMI-LETHAL
FAULTY XMAS LIGHTS
INSTALLATIONS
& ELECTRICAL GENERATOR
TRIP HAZARDS

**Prizes Presented by Sixty-Nine Page Three Girls Dressed As Santa Claus
No Beards. No Knickers.**

Prison Cabaret

Best Card Tricks of E-Wing
vs
Best Rope Tricks of A-Wing

—

SIR JIMMY SAVILE (DECEASED) ABSOLUTELY FINAL MORGUE TO GRAVE CHARITY FUN RUN

FUNEREAL TRACKSUIT BY ADIDAS

Post Event Nibbles by the Staff Canteen at Stoke Mandeville's National Spinal Injuries Centre
Tee-Total Celebrity Tributes by assorted Old Celebrities (t.b.c.)

—

COLD BLOODED
DANCE SENSATION

Saif al–Islam Gaddafi by Live Video Link-Up
with International Criminal Court

A SERIES OF ENTERTAINING IDIOTS

Tamara & Petra Ecclestone

VISIT

OCCUPY LONDON
Offering SUPPORT, MAKEOVERS,
Tanning Appointments & Pet Pedicures

plus

Debate Between The Bishop of London Dr. Richard Chartres & an Antelope

—

"Let the Gorenival Begin"

ABSOLUTELY WITLESS JOYLESS
& MORONIC
HALLOWEEN DRESS-UP
IN WESTMINSTER

Inc. David Cameron as Jack the Ripper, George Osborne as Jack the Ripper, William Hague as Jack the Ripper, Theresa May as Jack the Ripper, Nick Clegg as Jack the Ripper, Michael Gove as Jack the Ripper, Andrew Lansley as Jack the Ripper, Vince Cable as Jack the Ripper and Kenneth Clarke as Jack the Ripper. Plus Special Guest Appearance by ENGLAND as Mary Jane Kelly.

**Late-Capitalist Bible Class /
Free Market Theatre**

presents

Jesus &
The Money-Lenders

(Modern Day Re-Telling for Financial Services Sector)

plus

"A New Take On Rich Men
& The Eye of a Needle"

No Plastic Surgery or Excessive Dieting Necessary

&

God Was A Banker

Finding De-Regulation Allegory in the Bible

GREEK REFERENDUM ON THE TRUE NATURE OF ECONOMIC REALITY

ONE BANK ACCOUNT IN CREDIT: ONE VOTE

EUROZONE PHILOSOPHERS IN PANIC

LOOSELY DEFINED
CHINESE-THEME BUFFET

MUZAKAL INTERLUDE BY NANA MOUSKOURI

PLANS FOR AN ATTACK ON OR INVASION OF IRAN LED BY THE UNITED STATES

&

SUPPORTED BY THE USUAL SUSPECTS

SET TO MUSIC BY WAGNER

plus

NIGHT & DAY

SONGS FROM THE GUANTANAMO
TORTURE PLAYLIST

INTERPRETED BY SIR CLIFF RICHARD
WITH STRING ARRANGEMENTS BY ABD AL-RAHIM AL NASHIRI

Papandreou & The Sirens

The Sirens were magical sea creatures that looked rather like ~~mermaids~~ institutional investors specialising in sovereign debt.
They were known for their beautiful ~~singing voices~~ holiday homes, preposterous surgery-and-exercise-addicted wives and greed.
The music they made was so hypnotic that sailors stopped sailing their ~~ships~~ parliaments, to listen. With no one in charge, the ~~ships~~ parliaments crashed into land, killing everyone on board.

When ~~Odysseus~~ Papandreou heard the beautiful music, he was suspicious immediately.
He had had quite a few ~~adventures~~ economic meltdowns already.
He was beginning to be a bit suspicious of everything!

To be extra safe, he stuffed his ~~crewmen's~~ countrymen's ears so they could not hear the music.
He tied himself to the ship's mast with the idea of a referendum.
That way, in case the ~~gods~~ I.M.F. and the E.U. decided to be helpful, he wanted to be able to hear them.
But, since he was tied tightly, he would not be able to jump off the ship or swim ~~to shore~~ out of the Eurozone, or to do anything else that might endanger himself or his crew, when he heard the magical music.

Next Episode:

French president Sarkozy chains Antonis Samaras to a rock & German Merkel eats Samras' Liver
and it re-grows overnight and then Merkel eats it again.
Meanwhile Finance Minister Evangelos Venizelos (a Greek) is put in a maze
with a ~~one-eyed creature~~ half-man half-Bull called ~~The Minotaur~~ Berlusconi (Italy)
who disguises himself as a Swan to seduce Moroccan strippers.
In ~~Cannes~~ Troy George Osborne (England) calls a meeting of the G20
insisting that ~~European leaders~~ Theseus can solve the crisis.

Despite the warnings of Priam's daughter Cassandra, ~~Achilles~~ Papandreou and arch rival Venizelos have a battle.
Knowing that Papandreou's ~~heel~~ fiscal policy is the only part of his body
which is not invulnerable to damage by human weaponry ~~Paris~~ Venizelos attacks him there with a poison arrow.
Later he faces the ~~Cyclops Minotaur~~ electorate and follows a long thread (string or twine)
to finally get out of the terrible ~~Maze~~ Euro.

Movie version by Alan Smithee. Music & Costumes by the Cabaret Voltaire (Switzerland).

Cautious Noises
Dearth & Deficit
Unremitting Gloom

PLUS

EROTIC BALLOON TRICKS & POST-APOCALYPSE FACE PAINTING
CHOCOLATE FIREWORK FOUNTAIN (MAY CONTAIN NUTS)
SEMI-PRO CLOWNS & PRO-AM STRIPPERS
CHARITY 'BACKWARDS KIDS' CABARET (PARTIALLY OPEN MIC)

BEST OF THE INTERNET

FIREWORK PRANK VIDEOS

Inc. Rocket on a Rottweiler
'Bus Stop of the Catherine Wheels'
Angry Dad with Hand Blown Off
Hoodies' Roman Candle Penis Prank (Hilarious)
City Council Jobsworths vs Unexpected Air Bombs
Fire in a Post Box
Wheelie Bin Apocalypse

Inc. 12,000 powerful multi-directional rockets with ear wrecking 'big burst' © multi-effects, Spinning 'Chinese' Fountains, Red Napalm, Devil Head Shooter, Glitter Balls, Crackleburst, Purple Nova, Bin Laden Head, Sky Spunker, Angel Dust, & Fukishima (sic) Gold Rush

PLUS

Cellar Filled with Cats, Toddlers & Barrage-Pack Bangers

—

ALL YORKSHIRE

LATE NIGHT ROOFTOP
FIREWORK THROWING CONTEST

Who Can Hit a Pensioner?

Remember. Keep a firework in a closed box. Follow the instruction on a firework. Stand well back. Do no pretend Firework is coming out of your Arse. Do No Eat Firework. Do No Juggle Firework.

Esoteric / Existential Conflict

ALL TIME HIGHS
vs
ALL TIME LOWS

plus

"MONDAY NIGHT IS DRUNK FIGHT"

Old Mods
vs
Ancient Rockers

Loser Stays On. Win a Shaking Stevens Cassette or alternative t.b.c.

—

J.G. Ballard Tribute Events Continued
Car Crashes in Unnatural Fog
Now With 34 Vehicles PLUS Old School Autopsy Porn

Good News for Euro-Economy

Dr. Conrad Murray Prepares Medical Treatments For Italy in General

&

Silvio Berluscono (sic) in Particular

WITH BACKING OF THE I.M.F.

EUROSTATE DOMINOES /

CARNIVALE

OF

COLLAPSE

feat.

SLEEP DEPRIVED
ZOMBIE POLITICIANS OF EUROPE

& Podium Speeches in Tongues

plus

IMPRUDENT WHISPERS OF NICOLAS SARKOZY

SET TO MUSIC BY A GYPSY ORCHESTRA

—

BRITAIN'S GOT OBESE TALENT
BRITAIN'S GOT FLATULENT TALENT
BRITAIN'S GOT ANOREXIC TALENT
BRITAIN'S GOT MINDLESS WITLESS TALENT
BRITAIN'S GOT DESPERATE TALENT

& other talents t.b.c.

IRANIAN HEAVY METAL
&
INTERNATIONAL
DOUBLE DIP DISCO

feat. all the TOP DJs from Italy & Greece

—

WORLD ECONOMY
IDIOTIC
SUGGESTIONS
BOX

BEST SUGGESTION WINS A GUN, A LETHAL DOSE OF PROFAPANOL (sic)
OR THE BED THAT MICHAEL JACKSON DIED IN

James Murdoch

NINE-HOUR MONOLOGUE
CONCERNING
THINGS HE DOES NOT KNOW ABOUT
THINGS HE DID NOT KNOW ABOUT
THING HE NEVER HEARD ABOUT
THINGS HE ONLY RECENTLY HEARD ABOUT
THINGS HE NEVER IMAGINED
& etc.

FREE ADMISSION

—

Museum of Codswallop
Museum of Horseshit
Museum of Old Cobblers

BAD LOGIC

FOOLISH SENTIMENTS

&

STRICTLY ENFORCED
MACHO
THREE-MINUTE SILENCES

—

IN THE BASEMENT

EMERGENCY
INTERNAL GASTRIC
COSMETIC RE-DECORATION

WAGS & UNACCOMPANIED IDIOTS GO FREE

Teenage Girl Dance Troupe
present

SOFT FOCUS POWER-MAD
VIAGRA-FUELLED LECHERY PAGEANT

"ARRIVEDERCI L'AMORE" THE LIFE, LINGERIE & LOVES OF SILVIO BERLUSCONI

May Include Choreography

Guest Appearances by Noemi Letizia, Patrizia D'Addario and Karima el-Mahroug / Ruby Rubacuori

Directed by Nicole Minetti

With Silvio Berlasconi (sic) as Himself

& feat. Fresh Hand-Picked Selection of Approx 3,000 Talented Teens from Top Italian Model Agencies, Beauty Contests, Escort Agencies, Orphanages, Strip Clubs & TV Shows

Music excerpted from Handel's Messiah

Special Guests Tony Blair, Muammar Gaddafi (Deceased), A.C. Milan & Vladimir Putin

"WE ARE NOT ALONE"

WORLD FINANCIAL CRISIS SHOWS SIGNS OF INTELLIGENT LIFE

Reports from Experts at N.A.S.A., M.I.T., I.M.F., European Bank etc.

plus

CARNIVAL OF EXTINCT ANIMALS

Inc. Mammoth, Dodo, Free Press, Workers' Rights etc.

PRO-CELEBRITY LUNG TRANSPLANTS

—

AN EVENING OF FAILED ROCKET LAUNCHES, CANCELLED FLIGHTS, & SATELLITE MALFUNCTIONS

Music by David Bowie's Uncle's Cousin. Official Sponsor: Quantas.

—

HEAD TO TOE
CAR SPRAY PAINT
BODY ART
CONTEST

WHO CAN PAINT THEIR BEST FRIEND FASTEST?

ALL CONTESTANTS MUST BE DRUNK
ALL PARTICIPANTS / SPRAY PAINT MODELS MUST BE STONED

PRIZES PRESENTED BY HONOR BLACKMAN & BOB THE BUILDER

ZUCCOTTI PARK RE-OPENS
FOR (PRE-OCCUPY) BUSINESS AS USUAL
PEOPLE IN GREY, BLACK OR DARK BLUE SUITS
BRING A WRAP & A COFFEE
& SIT LOOKING VACANT
WHILE THE OCCASIONAL HOMELESS GUY
SHITS HIS PANTS
OR ASKS FOR CHANGE
& OTHER VICTORIES
FOR PUBLIC HEALTH
THE ECONOMY & SANITY

PLUS

AT THE WINDOWS
SMIRKING BANKERS
IN CHOREOGRAPHED
SELF-RIGHTEOUSNESS

RHETORICAL ESCAPOLOGY

OPPOSING PAIRS OF POLITICIANS BOUND TOGETHER USING ROPES MADE FROM THEIR OWN ARGUMENTS

plus

LIVE FROM THE INTERNATIONAL NAUGHTY CORNER

PRESIDENT BASHAR AL-ASSAD OF SYRIA
& DWINDLING SUPPORT

—

1 MILLION JOBLESS YOUTHS IN CONCERT
SING SONGS FROM THE TORY PARTY SONGBOOK

Inc. "ON YER BIKE", "NOT FOR TURNING", "CHAMPAGNE SUPERNOVA" etc.
DRASTICALLY REDUCED ORCHESTRAL ARRANGEMENTS by JEREMY HUNT

RETAIL GLOOM

Set to Music by Boris Karloff
With Olde Fog by Charles Dickens

plus

FASTER THAN LIGHT BANCRUPTCY (sic)

EXPERIMENTS CONFIRM IT IS POSSIBLE

—

Recreation of a Dream
Starring
Jane Mansfield (deceased)
as Lindsay Lohan
& Someone that looks like Rupert Murdoch
but it is not Rupert Murdoch

ALL DAY & ALL NIGHT
MOVIE DOUBLE BILL

ANN MIGRAINE
&
RICK PERISTALSIS
in

SYRIAN HOLIDAY

plus

MICHAEL QUININE
&
ASHLEIGH VERBIAGE
in

LOSING WEIGHT
THROUGH
ELECTIVE SURGERY

(Public Information Film)
Directed by Lars Von Trier

Films Projected Sumultaneously (sic). Films in 2-D Bring Your Own 3-D Glasses.

Ballet Of Uncomfortably Slow Movements

Inc. Blokes with Arthritis, Tranquilised Sleepwalkers,
Blind Depressives, Exhausted Old Women with Devastating Stomach Wounds,
Sufferers from a Terrible Ennui, Kids with Partial Parylisis (sic) & 200 Scousers in a Junkie Near-Coma

L.S.E. Lecture Series

Saif al-Islam Gaddafi
On the Current State of Libyan Justice

Winner of the Three Broken Fingers Humanitarian Prisoners Award

—

Egyptian Street Theatre

'Tales of Tahrir Square'

The Wanna Be Democratic Sensation Back by Popular Demand / Must End at Christmas

feat. All New Double Chorus
Inc. Corpses, Wounded Extras & Trigger Happy Troops

—

Homeless Beggars of Coventry

present

A Live ALL NUDE
Re-Enactment of SOD'S LAW

Cancelled Guest Appearance. Delayed Orchestra. Refreshments Land Face Down.

LARGE-SCALE COMMUNITY OPERA ABOUT GLOBAL WARMING
WITH A CONFUSING & LARGELY UNNECESSARY
SUBTITLED TRANSLATION INTO 'JAMAICAN PATOIS'
TO HELP BRING THE WORK TO A WIDER AUDIENCE

Music & Book by Prince Far I (Deceased)

—

**YOUNG MEN & WOMEN
GIVING OFF
BAD AEROSOL SMELL
&
MIXED MESSAGES**

—

Serious Mental Problems Theatre Group

present

THE PHAROHS (sic) RETURN
& BRING ORDER TO EGYPT

plus

LIFE STORY OF AN ORDINARY
LIBYAN CAMEL HERDER

Starring Partial Saif al-Islam Gaddafi Look-A-Like as 'The Herder'. Funded by The National Lottery.

NEAR DEATH EXPERIENCES
RE-ENACTED BY SCARY LOOKING KIDS WITH GLOVE PUPPETS
& 'COMPLICTATED (sic) FACIAL EXPRESSIONS'

BEST OF INTERNET #83

HOME-MADE EXPLOSIONS RECIPES

&

D.I.Y. FACELIFTS

—

CELEBRITY DOG FIGHTS

PARIS HILTON'S POODLE
vs
KIM KARDASHIAN'S CHIHUAHUA

P. DIDDY'S ROTTWEILER
vs
VIN DIESEL'S GERMAN SHEPHERD

—

EGYPT IN LIMBO – THEMED DISCO

FREAKY TRANCEY RAVEY DANCE MUSIC & GUNSTEP

Field Marshal Hussein Tantawi Explains Democracy to 30 Dead Protesters

(Partial Re-enactment of a Previous Explanation by Hosni Mubarak)

—

Battle of Euro-Stereotypes

French Nonsense
vs
Dutch Pragmatism

German Money
vs
Italian Disorganisation

English Stiff Upper Lips
vs
Polish Plumbers

Minimalist Animal Sculptures

Inc. Stray Dogs Balanced in a Pyramid

Cats in a Bag

Rabbits in a Hole

Stacked Pigeons & etc.

Sponsored by R.S.P.C.A. / R.N.I.B. & R.I.B.A. Prizes Awarded by Morrissey.

Politicians & Public Servants
COMPULSORY CHARITY INCARCERATION

CAGED FOR A DAY

PLUS

TOP TEN LEAST-FAVOURITE B-LIST CELEBS
SWEAR A LIFE LONG VOW OF UNSPONSORED SILENCE

Government Youth Beggar Program

present

Songs from Oliver Twist

Dickens' Amazing Musical Brought to Life in Streets of London

Inc. Hit Songs Old Man River, Chitty Chitty Bang Bang, Obla Di Obla Da, Underneath the Arches, We Built This City on Rock n Roll, Persian Rent Boy, Polish Plasterer, Moldovan Waitress & Ukrainian Mini–Cab

plus

All 18-25 Year Olds Given Free Govt. Beggar-Sign & Cup / Hat for Coin Collection

—

**PRE–OLYMPIC ENTERTAINMENT
FREE CONCERT OF RACIST FOOTBALL SONGS**

Bring Your Own Prejudices. Best Monkey Chants Win a Banana.

—

**Egypt's Supreme Council of the Armed Forces
Explains Plans to Run Italy, Portugal, Spain & Iceland**

Saturday Lecture

QUANTUM DISENCHANTMENT

Depressed Scientists from the Hadron Collider Team
Explain how Heartbreak Travels Faster than Light

Guest Appearance by Kelly Brook's Sister's Best Friend's Neighbour's Cat

—

Pre-Teens Greenhouse Gases Contest:
Who Can Breathe in the Most?

& Other Experiments Inc. Hand in Bunsen Burner,
Sulphur Nose, Ice Testicles, Biro in Eye, Electric Doorhandle
& Advanced Decomposition of an Adidas Bag

plus free download

TEN THOUSAND MILLION TRILLION IRRELEVANT OLD SONGS

Sunday Lecture

QUANTUM DISENCHANTMENT
Part Two 3-D

Even More Depressed Scientists from the Hadron Collider Team
Explain again how Heartbreak Travels Faster than Light

Repeat Guest Appearance by Kelly Brook's Sister's Best Friend's Neighbour's Cat (cancelled)

PLUS

QUANTUM DISENCHANTMENT
PART THREE 4-D
"GIVE 'EM ENOUGH SUPER STRING THEORY & THEY WILL HANG THEMSELVES"

SUICIDAL Scientists from the Hadron Collider Team

Explain FOR THE THIRD TIME how Heartbreak Travels Faster than Light

Inc. 3rd TIME LUCKY Repeat Guest Appearance by Kelly Brook's Sister's Best Friend's Neighbour's Cat

(ALSO Cancelled)

INTERNATIONAL PEACE, LOVE & XANAX

(Now with anxiolytic, sedative, hypnotic, skeletal muscle relaxant, anticonvulsant, & amnestic properties.)

—

Dr. George Osborne

SCRUBS UP & SEDATES ENGLAND READY FOR A HUGE FISCAL INJECTION

—

HOT TICKET

Experimental Egyptian Ballet of Armoured Ballot Boxes

Choreographed by

Field Marshal Mohamed Hussein Tantawi & Co.

THE
COLD
LIGHT
OF
DAY

**ALL THE TIME EVERYWHERE FOREVER.
WARTS & ALL. NO HOLDS BARRED.**

HOT TICKET ONE MAN SHOW

RUSSIAN DEMOCRACY
BY VLADIMIR PUTIN

DIRECTED BY PUTIR VLADIMIN
STARRING VLADIMIR PUTIN
BASED ON A NOVEL BY PUTIR VLADIMIN

VOTING CHOREOGRAPHED BY LENI RIEFENSTAHL & UNITED RUSSIA

Interval Entertainment by Anna Chapman & Mikhail Borisovich Khodorkovsky
Suits by Sergio Leone
Music by the Balalaika Orchestra of Siberia

—

UNDERAGE DRINKING & DRIVING CONTEST
UNDERAGE SEX & SMOKING CONTEST
UNDERAGE FIREARMS OFFENCES
UNDERAGE VOTING
UNDERAGE ROADRAGE

—

A VISITOR'S GUIDE TO THE BRITISH EMBASSY IN TEHRAN

TRUE WINTER

Inc. Emotional Memory & The Right to Bare Arms

—

'2 Minute Lecture Series'

UNSUSTAINABLE TOURISM
UNSUSTAINABLE VIOLENCE
UNSUSTAINABLE BITTERNESS
UNSUSTAINABLE DIPLOMACY
UNSUSTAINABLE IDIOCY

—

MINOR–CELEBUTANTE DIVORCES ON ICE

PLUS

PUBLIC SECTOR BOWEL MOVEMENTS / UNSYMPATHETIC CELEBRITY STRIKE ACTION

With Compère Prole Suntan & Derelict Gazebo

Sponsored by The Marquis of Gramby & The Institute of Forgetting

THE CARPET PULLED RIGHT OUT FROM UNDER PEOPLE WITHOUT WARNING

ALL DAY & ALL NIGHT / FOREVER

—

Jeremy Clarkson Starving To Death at the Front & Back of a Never Ever Diminishing Queue at U.K. Immigration

A MACHINE FOR TURNING LOVE INTO ICE

Prototype Only / Beta Testing Version. Full Working Model Coming Soon.
Guaranteed Results Over Long, Medium & Short Distances

December 4 2011

A
BLACK
HOLE

No Intermission

Flat-Pack Melancholia

For Easy Transportation

Manual Self-Assembly Units in Variety of Sizes
(Only Colour: Black)
Set-Up Requires Extra Tools / Spare Parts Not Included
Trans-Continental 24:7 Premium Rate 'Cry for Help' Line

PLUS

SPECIAL OFFER

Buy Two Flat-Pack Melancholias

& Get an Inflatable Depression

(worth £24.99) for FREE

**Not Suitable for Use in Swimming Pool, Ocean or Lido
Not Suitable for Use in Sex-Play or by Pets & Kids Under 8**

AUSTERITY THEMED NO LIGHTS NO HEATING & NO FOOD ECONOMY XMAS PARTY

feat. AURTISTIC (sic) CABARET / DRUNK SANTA

Old Songs, Old Jokes & Imitation Logs on a Hideous Non–Functioning Fire

—

D.I.Y. Euro Stabilization

—

"SELF LACERATION"

A PATHETIC COMEDY OF NON-CONSENSUAL
SEASONALLY ADJUSTED LIVING ARRANGEMENTS

LIMBO DANCING FOR THE LONELY: TIME SLOWED DOWN TO 16rpm

—

'EXTREME' TEAM BUILDING
Inc. KNIFE, TASER, GIN & GRAVITY GAMES,
GUNS & LIVE AMMUNITION

—

THINK-TANK

Getting The Dead Back to Work / Do They Really Need Funerals?

plus sessions on

Chemotherapy Workfare
Sustainable Power Solutions from Epilepsy
Singing For Your Supper

With Presentations by Prof. M. Harrington & Co.
Music by Ryanair. Lighting by Aldi.

U.K. TRIPLE-A RATING

Amnesia (Collective & Romantic)

Anaesthesia (Local, General & Compulsory)

Arrhythmia (Intellectual & Emotional)

plus

"IMPENDING EMPTINESS FOREVER"

A Cheering Interlude of
Partially Choreographed Dolphins

or 'whatever the fuck you like'

—

**EUROSEPTIC DISCO
PAY TO GET OUT**

EUROVISION SONG CONTEST
STRICT NEW RULES
& PENALTIES ANNOUNCED

Judges: Sarkozy, Merkel, Standards & Poor
Imaginary Veto: Cameron

With Entries from Fiscal Compact (Germany), Sovereign Debt (Italy), Rioting Lunatics (Greece) & Splendid Isolation (U.K.)

a) Each performance may consist of a maximum of six people on stage.
No live animals shall be allowed on stage.

b) All ~~artists~~ Governments competing in a Semi-Final must be solvent and aged at least 16 on the day of the Final.
All artists competing only in the Final must be aged at least 16 on the day of the Final.

c) No ~~artist~~ Government may compete for more than one ~~country~~
Ratings Agency ~~in the E.S.C.~~ in a given year.

d) Each ~~Participating Broadcaster~~ Government is free to ~~decide~~ enforce the language
in which its artist(s) will sing. No LOVE SONGS. No Comical songs.

e) Artists shall perform live on stage, accompanied by a recorded backing-track
which contains no vocals of any kind or any vocal imitations or any kind of music.
The ~~Host Broadcaster~~ Government shall verify respect for this rule.

f) Changes to the lyrics, the artist or group (including its name), the title of the song
and the language of the performance (i.e. all elements which appear in printed material such as brochures,
CD covers and booklets) shall be allowed only up until the date of the Final
or the Collapse of the Euro, whichever is sooner.

g) The lyrics and / or performance of the songs shall not bring the Shows,
~~the E.S.C. as such or the E.B.U.~~ or the E.U. into disrepute. No lyrics, speeches, gestures of a political or
similar nature shall be permitted during the Show. No swearing, speaking in Romany
or other unacceptable language shall be allowed in the lyrics or in the performances of the songs.
No commercial messages or threats of popular revolution of any kind shall be allowed.
A breach of this rule may result in disqualification.

CONTORTIONIST'S CABARET OF FEELINGS THAT HAVE SUPPOSEDLY DIED

NO SUPPORT

INTERNATIONAL MODERN BALLET

KIND WORDS FALLING ON DEAF EARS

FOREVER OR FOR ETERNITY
WHICHEVER IS THE LONGEST & COLDEST

—

In the Basement

APOCALYPTO CYCLOGENESIS
PUNITIVE EURO EXERCISE REGIME
WATERED DOWN CLIMATE CHANGE AGREEMENTS

plus

GUEST APPEARANCE BY IRRELEVANT BYSTANDERS

PARADE OF WORTHLESS INDIVIDUALS

plus

UNFORGIVABLE BULLSHIT IN CONCERT

FREE ENTRANCE. EASY EXIT.

—

**AMNESIAC HOUSEWARMING
(FORGET EVERYTHING)**

FAKE DELIBERATIONS
OF A RIGGED JURY

A FESTIVAL OF POOR MANAGEMENT & INSUFFICIENT REGULATION

—

In The Basement

Damaging Gusts of Artificial Wind

Footballers & Rock Stars
VS
Inner Demons

Cold Hearted Lovers
Smother Each Other With A Blanket Of Contempt

PEOPLE TALKING BUT NOT REALLY LISTENING TO EACH OTHER

—

CHEAP & NOT NECESSARILY CHEERFUL

"MARRIAGE OF VETO"
TWO SPEED EURO-OPERA

—

CRAPPY 4TH WALL DRAMA CO.

present

DAILY & DOMESTIC

plus

Higgs Bosun (sic)

(Partial Appearance t.b.c.)

A FIGHT STAGED
BETWEEN A UNICORN
&
A PREDATOR DRONE

—

UNCONSCIOUS REVELATIONS
OF A PARTIALLY SEDATED DIPLOMAT

—

DISTRESSING VIDEOS OF THE INTERNET

feat.

FRESH MEAT & INFECTED BULLET WOUNDS
ALL NEW TORTURE PORN FROM SYRIA

—

MODERN LANGUAGES

TWO FOR ONE CUT PRICE SPECIAL
FRANCOPHONE GERMANY / GERMANIC FRANÇAIS

—

All New Adventures Beyond The Last Visible Dog

In The Scheiss-Medallion Food Court

AN XMAS CHORUS OF DEFECTIVE ANIMATRONIC SANTAS SING 'ROHDOLP THAT REED KNOWS RAINDIRE' IN A BLIZZARD OF SEMI-TOXIC SNOW

PLUS

SOPHISTICATED REMOTE CONTROL BOMB-DISPOSAL ROBOTS
TOY WITH, CUT & PROBE AT THE CORPSE OF AN INFANT LYING PRONE
TO SEE IF THERE IS SOMETHING HIDDEN INSIDE

BLOOD
EVERYWHERE

&

THE SOUND
OF
AMPLIFIED
RAIN

XMAS SPECIAL OFFER
NO HOLDS BARRED
EVERYTHING MUST GO

ISOLATION CHAMBER XMAS & NEW YEAR

plus

POWER-SAVING LIGHT-AUSTERITY

COMPULSORY EXTENSION OF DARKNESS & NIGHTTIME

HOURS OF DAYLIGHT IN EACH EUROZONE COUNTRY CALCULATED IN PROPORTION TO SIZE OF BORROWING / DEFICIT & G.D.P.

(BASELINE ESTIMATES: GREECE IN TOTAL DARKNESS, GERMANY WITH DAYLIGHT 24/7)

LONELY PEOPLE AT XMAS VOLUNTARY EUTHANASIA PROGRAM

Sponsored by Harrods, Aldi, the D.H.S.S. & the R.S.P.C.A.

Lethal Mercy-Killing Cocktail Injections Administered by a Team of Celebrity Volunteers

Inc. Norman Lamont, Amy Childs, Woody Allen, Carla Bruni, Sharon Osborne & Margaret Thatcher

—

Tory Nazi / Nazi Tory / Tory Nazi

Cross-dressing Idiots' Ski-Wear Fetish Party

—

Battle in the Aether

Dear Leader Kim Jong-il (Deceased)

vs

Vaclav Havel (Deceased)

SLOW DEATH /
A BLACK HOLE*

*BASED ON A PREVIOUS HOLE BUT BIGGER & MORE POWERFUL

—

SONGS OF FAMINE,
ECONOMIC DISASTER,
REPRESSION
& NUCLEAR 'DIPLOMACY'

feat. ONE MILLION WEEPING PEDESTRIANS
Starring KIM-JONG-IL (DECEASED) & KIM JONG-UN

Choreographed by Busby Berklay (sic) (Deceased)
Plus Tearful TV Announcers, Angry Sobbing Men in Suits & Apparently Broken Hearted Teenagers

—

11 Days of National Boredom

DISCOUNT BREAST ENHANCMENT FOR PENSIONERS

EMOTIONAL AMPUTATION FOR BEGINNERS

FREE XMAS OFFER

FULL COLOUR JIGSAW OF SUBATOMIC SPACE

(ACTUAL SIZE)

plus

NEW YEAR ADVANCE PURCHASE SPECIAL

FULL COLOUR JIGSAW OF A PULVERIZED FACE

(1:10 SCALE)

NON-PREVENTATIVE MEDICINE

—

SEASONAL SONGS OF THE WORLD ORCHESTRA
PERFORMED BY A CHOIR OF RACIST TRAFFIC COPS

EGYPTIAN DEMOCRACY IN PROGRESS

WOMEN–BEATING CONTEST

TWO POINTS FOR A CRACKED SKULL / FIVE POINTS FOR TOPLESS

December 22 2011

WIVES OF THE WAR DEAD XMAS NUMBER ONE DIRGE

feat. Widows of Servicemen
Killed in Afghanistan, Iraq, N. Ireland & The Gulf

Musical Arrangements by Heckler & Koch, Lockheed Martin & B.A.E. Systems
Styling by a Next Door Neighbour of a Man behind the Pussycat Dolls
Choreography by Francis Bacon (Deceased). Cover Art by Pablo Picasso (Deceased).
Lyrics by Wilfred Owen (Deceased). Percentage of Proceeds to a Landmine Charity.

—

TOP TEN RACIST MUTTERINGS OF PROFESSIONAL FOOTBALLERS
(CREATIVE INTERPRETATION BY AMATEUR LIP-READERS)

feat. Luis Suarez & Special Guests t.b.c

—

GARDENERS' QUESTIONTIME FUKUSHIMA SPECIAL – MASSIVE VEG & MUTANT PARASITES

A LITTLE BIT OF
YULETIDE BITTERNESS
DOES YOU GOOD

—

Inexplicable Ritual Blinding
Of A Department Store Santa Claus

Not Entirely Suitable for Children

plus

Sexually Suggestive Stage Routines
of Snow White & the Seventeen-Inch Dwarves

Starring a Woman that Used to be Attractive & the Half-Brother of a Man who was Once in 'Holby City'

—

Room Filled With Economic Gloom
Free Admission

—

Best Holiday-Season Car Bombs
#1 Baghdad

XMAS ECZEMA CHARITY SPECIAL

SHIT IN THE SHAPE OF A NOVELTY ORNAMENT

Inc. GOOD KING WENCELESSLASS (sic), DONKEY MANGER, BRUCE FORSYTH'S BRAIN & ELIZABETH HURELY'S (sic) BREASTS

—

PSYCHIC CENTRIFUGE

Free Rides. Management Not Responsible for Consequences, Illness or Lost Property.

—

IMPRESSIONS OF SYRIA

Post-Colonial Holiday Snaps & Choreography of Carnage Set to Music by Marvin Bentwhistle & Navraj Gyroscope

—

"Joined Up Thinking"

Xmas Special

All Day Four-Course Menu / One Price Suits All

Love in Formaldehyde
Hope in Formaldehyde
Faith in Formaldehyde
Trust in Formaldehyde

plus choice of dessert

Total Reduction of Rehydrated Nothingness
Non-consensual Chargrilled Optimism
or
Simulated Fruit Juice (May Contain Excrement)

—

ON THE YULETIDE SPECIAL BIG SCREEN

Celebrity Chest Pains
Jabberwocky 7 vs Intelligentsia
Inside Prince Phillipe (sic)
Twat Team Cameron: Brokeback Britain
Tanks for Memories (Repeat)
Anything for Money (Repeat)
Call Me Vesuvius (Roman Drama Repeat)
DVD Pirates of The Caribbean (Illegal Download)
Putin Forever (Repeat)
Margaret Thatcher (Deceased Please)
Hypocritical Breakfast (Alternate Reality Contest)
Mistletoe & Barrister (Paralegal Posh Detectives)
Chav Swap (Idiots)
Am-Dram Brain Swap (Total Fucking Idiots)

plus

Boiling Water on Open Wounds

TRAUMA EXACERBATED BY FAMINE

SHODDY WORKMANSHIP EXACERBATED BY LOW GRADE MATERIALS

ENDEMIC POVERTY EXACERBATED BY INDUSTRIAL POLLUTION

ABYSMAL AUTOMATED TELEPHONE BOOKING SYSTEMS
EXACERBATED BY CONCEALED CREDIT-CARD SURCHARGES

WEAK & OTHERWISE NONSENSICAL DEMOCRACY
EXACERBATED BY AGGRESSIVE NON-STATE ACTORS & TRANSNATIONAL CAPITAL

WOLVES EXACERBATED BY JACKALS

POOR EDUCATION EXACERBATED BY RELENTLESS ASSET STRIPPING

MENTAL ILLNESS EXACERBATED BY PHYSICAL ABUSE

UBIQUITOUS SURVEILLANCE EXACERBATED BY COLLECTIVE AMNESIA

TORTURE EXACERBATED BY OBESITY

MENTAL RAPE EXACERBATED BY FACTORY FARMING

SUICIDE BOMBERS EXACERBATED BY CLIMATE CHANGE

INFLATION EXACERBATED BY BLOOD POISONING

INDIFFERENCE EXACERBATED BY SEXUAL DYSFUNCTION

HALF-BAKED ARGUMENTS EXACERBATED BY A TENDENCY TO VAGUENESS

CLASS DIVISION EXACERBATED BY CONSTANT RAIN

MASS HALLUCINATION EXACERBATED BY MASS HYSTERIA

December 27 2011

MEN DRINKING, PISSING, SHITTING & CRYING AT THE SAME TIME

DEPRESSION KARAOKE (Repeat)

PATIENTS THAT ARE SLIPPING IN & OUT OF CONSCIOUSNESS

—

XMAS PARTY GAME SPECIAL

Inc. SCISSOR RACES, PRIVATISED HEALTH SERVICE, EGG BAITING, PIN A KNIFE IN THE GRANDCHILDREN, TOTAL SENILITY SEARCH PARTY, PAPARAZZI!, DEREGULATED ECONOMY, YELLING AT TV (All Channels), HUNT THE DEBTOR, DRUGGED BALCONEERING, DRINK-FUELED INTERNATIONAL TENSION BUILD UP, BLINDFOLD OCTOGENARIAN STRIP TWISTER, EGYPTIAN DEMOCRACY, RAPID FORECLOSURE, PIN THE BLAME ON THE LABOUR PARTY, CLING-FILM TOILET BOWL, PEOPLE WHO REALLY LET YOU DOWN, GETTING ON & GETTING AHEAD & LATE-NIGHT EARLY-ONSET ALZHEIAMERS (sic) QUIZ

plus

Spotting Patterns in Nothingness
Strictly One Player Only. No Prizes.

—

YULETIDE LANDSCAPES OF EUROPE #4667289

WOMEN GATHER FIREWOOD, BOTTLES, CANS & HUMAN WASTE FOR POSSIBLE RE-SALE

KIDS SCRAPE GUTTERS FOR SCRAPS OF FOOD

The Worst Of The Worst
The Last Of The Best

—

RAISING OF THE SECURITY ALERT STATUS FROM GREEN TO YELLOW

RAISING OF THE SECURITY ALERT STATUS FROM YELLOW TO ORANGE

RAISING OF THE SECURITY ALERT STATUS FROM ORANGE TO RED

RAISING OF THE SECURITY ALERT STATUS
FROM RED TO SOME EVEN BRIGHTER
& MORE ALARMING COLOUR OF RED

—

DOGS WITH SHAVED BELLIES
MEN WITH TWISTED LEGS
WOMEN WITH SHAVED HEADS

—

The Battle of ~~Agincourt~~ Footlocker
& Other Pointless Christmas Murders t.b.c.

—

Love Sold Short by Cowards Who Style Themselves As Brave

COMING SOON

Golden Age of Rot
Golden Age of Riot
Golden Age of Night Terror
Golden Age of Avian Flu
Golden Age of Trembling
Golden Age of Inconstancy
Golden Age of Mutation
Golden Age of Sunblock
Golden Age of Lies
Golden Age of Privatised Prisons
Golden Age of Waters Rising
Golden Age of Ice in Veins
Golden Age of Arson
Golden Age of Recession
Golden Age of Waterboarding
Golden Age of Fluid Retention
Golden Age of Sedation
Golden Age of Landmark Shopping Malls
Golden Age of Partially Structured Fictional Situations Played Out As Reality
Golden Age of Total Indifference
Golden Age of Shivering
Golden Age of Myopia
Golden Age of Frozen Liquidity
Golden Age of Lovelessness
Golden Age of Intolerance
Golden Age of Legalese
Golden Age of Pornographic Violence
Golden Age of Repression
Golden Age of Industrial Silicon
Golden Age of Cancer
Golden Age of Abandonment
Golden Age of Shame
Golden Age of Nostalgia
Golden Age of Proxy War
Golden Age of Impotence
Golden Age of Burning Cars
Golden Age of Road Rage
Golden Age of Forgetting
Golden Age of Dreams for Sale

December 30 2011

VENUE CLOSED FOR DEMOLITION
VENUE CLOSED FOR UNCONVINCING RE-FURB
VENUE CLOSED FOR CONVERSION TO CAR PARK, SHOPPING MALL & BASEMENT TORTURE CENTRE
VENUE CLOSED DUE TO BOMB DAMAGE, ARSON & GAS LEAKS
VENUE CLOSED FOR PRIVATE REDEVELOPMENT
VENUE CLOSED DUE TO MENTAL INSTABILITY
VENUE CLOSED FOR LONG TERM DERELICTION
VENUE CLOSED FOR PERMANENT EXORCISM
VENUE CLOSED FOR NO REAL REASON
VENUE CLOSED DUE TO INTELLECTUAL STAGNATION
VENUE CLOSED DUE TO BULLYING
VENUE CLOSED FOR CONVERSION TO 120 'UNIQUE' LOFT-STYLE APPARTMENTS (sic)
VENUE CLOSED DUE TO TERROR THREATS
VENUE CLOSED DUE TO SERIOUS COMPRESSION ERRORS & ARTEFACTING
VENUE CLOSED DUE TO TOTAL LACK OF INTEREST
VENUE CLOSED FOR LEGAL REASONS
VENUE CLOSED FOREVER
VENUE CLOSED UNTIL FURTHER NOTICE
VENUE CLOSED DUE TO ILL HEALTH OF THE OWNER
VENUE CLOSED FOR JIHAD PRACTICE, INSANITY & DIVORCE
VENUE CLOSED DUE TO TERMINAL BOREDOM
VENUE CLOSED FOR 'PERSONAL REASONS'
VENUE CLOSED DUE TO FLOODING, KIDNAP, SUBSIDENCE & TAX EVASION
VENUE CLOSED FOR CONVERSION TO WELL-DODGY MASSAGE PARLOUR
VENUE CLOSED DUE TO CIVIL WAR, BAD DEBTS & D.O.S. ATTACKS
VENUE CLOSED FOR REDECORATION & PESTICIDAL TREATMENT
VENUE CLOSED DUE TO COMPLICATIONS ARISING AFTER A ROUTINE OPERATION
VENUE CLOSED DUE TO POLICE HARASSMENT
VENUE CLOSED DUE TO HEALTH & SAFETY VIOLATIONS
VENUE CLOSED DUE TO EXPIRY OF LEASE
VENUE CLOSED FOR CONVERSION TO NEW AGE CHURCH & PAINFULLY HIP COFFEE BAR
VENUE CLOSED DUE TO INCONTINENCE, BANKRUPTCY & PLAGUE OF STRAY DOGS
VENUE CLOSED FOR CONVERSION TO WASTELAND
VENUE CLOSED DUE TO WILFUL NEGLECT
VENUE CLOSED DUE TO UNEXPECTED HEARTBREAK
VENUE CLOSED DUE TO ELECTRICAL FAILURES
VENUE CLOSED DUE TO SOMETHING LIKE A DEATH IN THE FAMILY

OUT WITH THE OLD & IN WITH THE NEW

**WORTHLESS LONE & YEAR LONG DANCE ABOUT NOTHING
PERFORMED AT MIDNIGHT IN AN EMPTY HOUSE TO AN AUDIENCE OF NONE**

Vacuum Days is Over – You Have Been Watching

—

ABSOLUTELY NO THANKS TO ANYONE

THE JUDGE'S DECISION IS FINAL